0005980

KT-547-360

Death in Britain

How local mortality rates have changed: 1950s-1990s

Daniel Dorling
University of Bristol

July 1997

© Joseph Rowntree Foundation 1997

All rights reserved

Published by
Joseph Rowntree Foundation
The Homestead
40 Water End
York YO3 6LP

Tel: 01904 629241
Website: www.jrf.org.uk

ISBN 1 85935 031 3
Price £11.95

Designed by Adkins Design
Printed by Colorworks

Printed on recycled paper

JR
JOSEPH
ROWNTREE
FOUNDATION

Contents

Acknowledgements

The author is grateful to the Joseph Rowntree Foundation for funding the production of this report and, in particular, to Derek Williams for encouraging me to ensure that it was produced. The Foundation's advisory group provided many valuable comments on several drafts of this report as well as informal advice between meetings, and I am very grateful to them for this: Tony Champion, Christine Dunn, Steve Simpson, Jillian Smith and Russell Ecob. Jennifer Grundy and Joanne Warburton were the research assistants on the project, which could not have been completed without their help and perseverance with the published statistics.

Lastly, I am indebted to the staff of the Office for National Statistics and the General Register Office (Scotland) who provided the unpublished mortality data, in digital form, used to construct the remainder of this report.

Data from the Censuses of Population is Crown Copyright and is reproduced by permission of the Controller of Her Majesty's Stationery Office. It was accessed through the ESRC/JISC purchase. Data on mortality was kindly provided by the Office for National Statistics. The research this report is based on was also funded by the Economic and Social Research Council Health Variations Programme.

Summary of terms used in this report

absolute mortality rate	number of deaths divided by people at risk
crude death rate	mortality rates not standardised by age or sex
excess deaths	the number of extra people who die in a period than the national mortality rates would lead us to expect
life chances	refers to mortality rates in general
life expectancy	probable age of death
mortality rate	measures the chances of a person dying in a given period; represented as a percentage of the population at risk
standardised mortality ratios	a person's relative chance of dying each year in an area, accounting for the age and sex structure of the area

1 Introduction

Aims

Statistics about the probable age at which we will die (our life expectancy) provide the most striking evidence of problems in a society. The World Health Organization requires all countries to monitor changes in life expectancy by social group and geographical area as we approach the year 2000 (the reduction in inequalities by 25 per cent is known as Target One, and Britain is committed to achieve it). Whereas in the United Kingdom figures on changes by social group are available for most of this century using a consistent set of definitions, data on mortality using a consistent set of areas have to be constructed separately and are not easily available.

This report aims to discover how life chances (a term used to refer to mortality rates in general) have been changing for a constant set of local areas since World War II. The improvements in death rates for different age and sex groups are compared. The areas used are those for which standardised mortality ratios (a person's relative chance of dying each year in an area, accounting for the age and sex structure of the area) were published in the Registrar General's *Decennial Review* of 1951. Comparisons are based on a comparable set of official statistics to those of 1951, exploring how rates have changed in each subsequent decade.

Calculations are also made on the basis of contemporary administrative boundaries and for more recent dates (up to 1995), although records with detailed geographical location were only available up to 1992 because 1991 census data are needed to calculate rates.

Background

In some parts of Britain many people are dying prematurely. The general geographical pattern of average life expectancy is well known, being shorter in the north of Britain and in the inner areas of cities. What is not known is where death rates have fallen most over the long term, and thus whether the differences between areas are growing.

This information is not known because the boundaries of the areas for which official statistics are published have been changed so often. For example, in the 1950s one area of Britain where adults were most likely to die young was Shoreditch. In the 1960s that borough was abolished and absorbed into surrounding areas with higher life expectancy, so mortality rates appeared to improve there. It may well be the case, though, that this part of the country still has some of the highest mortality rates, and that people now living in the area which was Shoreditch are relatively worse off than they were forty years ago.

Previous research has concentrated on the different chances of dying of people assigned to socio-economic groups. This research has found that differences in chances of dying between socio-economic groups have gradually increased since the 1930s, i.e. overall rates of mortality have declined more rapidly for higher socio-economic groups.

There has been energetic debate as to the meaning and causes of this trend. A subject which has received relatively little consideration, however, is how people's chances of dying by their geographical (rather than social) position has altered over the period. With the establishment of the National Health Service (at the start of the period being considered here), resources have been distributed on a geographical basis and thus it may be assumed that, whatever occurs in different social groups, life chances should become more equitable by area. If this turns out not to be the case then a new facet to the debate is revealed and we need to consider why inequalities are rising according to where people live, as well as changing depending on their socio-economic position.

Methods

To prepare for this study, the changing levels of mortality were calculated for a consistent set of local areas in England, Wales and Scotland for the period from 1950 onwards using official records. The areas used are the County Boroughs, and urban and rural remainders of counties existing in 1951. They are shown in Appendix 1. A Geographical Information System was used to monitor boundary changes. Further details are given in the technical report,* which also gives more details of the statistics quoted in this report. These are usually either mortality rates expressed as a percentage, or rates standardised to allow for age-sex structure.

There is no easy explanation as to why mortality rates by area should be diverging or converging in different parts of the country. The scope of this report, however, is simply to monitor the extent to which these changes are occurring and to measure how unusual such changes are compared to past trends.

The technical report, *Changing life chances in Britain, 1950s to 1990s*, is available from the Department of Geography, University of Bristol, University of Bristol, University Road, Bristol BS8 1SS (price £11.95).

Past ratios can also be used to measure the degree of improvement in mortality rates in different parts of the country. By using a consistent set of areas and population sub-groups we can consider these changes without being concerned that the statistics are altered by changes to the boundaries or by techniques used to enumerate the population.

On the following pages a series of tables and maps summarise the areas of particularly low mortality and high mortality at the beginning and at the end of the period examined.

LIBRARY
PEMBURY HOSPITAL
01892 823535

Table 1 Areas with the ten **highest** and **lowest** excess deaths for males in 1950-53

Area	Infant	Children[1]		Adult	
		1-4	5-14	15-45	45-64
Scotland north and east					
Inverness			76		
Dundee					1191
Edinburgh	-153				1960
Scotland west and south					
Glasgow	1284	528	242	2428	9296
Lanark County		122		336	
North East					
Northumberland urban				431	
Durham urban	461			366	
Durham rural	421			532	
West Hartlepool		83			
Lancs/Yorks rural					
Lancashire rural				-148	
Yorkshire West Riding rural					-876
Yorkshire urban					
Hull	500				
Leeds					1722
Bradford	394				
Lancashire urban					
Lancashire urban	1192			388	3781
Salford				300	1945
Manchester	434			710	5163
Liverpool	715	406		1125	4532
East Midlands					
Lincolnshire Kesteven			99		
West Midlands					
Staffordshire urban	348	90	89		
Birmingham					1913
Wales					
Glamorganshire urban	491			850	2728
Montgomeryshire rural			74		
South West					
Bristol	-195				
Devon rural					-785
Wiltshire rural				-247	
South rural					
Kent rural					-809
Berkshire rural				-152	
Essex rural	-127				-747
Norfolk rural				-210	-1065
South urban					
Southampton urban	-157			-265	
Kent urban	-343	-65		-228	-1656
Surrey urban	-495	-57	-34	-473	-2642
Middlesex	-916	-224	-176	-1029	-3827
Hertfordshire urban	-170		-29	-172	-945
Essex urban	-446	-92	-35	-666	-2036
London					
Croydon	-128				

The highest and lowest three figures are shown in dark coloured blocks.
Note: 1. Because mortality is low in children only the highest and lowest five areas are shown.

Table 2 Areas with the ten **highest** and **lowest** excess deaths for males in 1990-92

Area	Infant	Children 1-4	5-14	Adult 15-45	45-64
Scotland north and east					
Perth		63			
Edinburgh				443	
Scotland west and south					
Glasgow				**1715**	**10047**
Lanark County				255	1179
North East					
Newcastle					1559
Durham Urban		-14			2398
Yorkshire urban					
Yorkshire West Riding urban		-27	-27	-273	
Leeds	140				
Bradford	163		104		1192
Halifax	96				
Doncaster		81			
Sheffield				-213	
Lancs/Cheshire urban					
Lancashire urban		-17	-42		2687
Blackburn	171				
Oldham			41		
Salford					1282
Manchester		102	123	496	**3921**
Liverpool			78		3005
Cheshire urban	-101	-19			
East Midlands					
Derby	94				
Nottingham	125		48		
West Midlands					
Staffordshire urban				-172	
Stoke-on-Trent	196				
Burton-on-Trent		96			
Birmingham	444				3122
Coventry	125				
Warwickshire urban				-170	
Wales					
Glamorganshire rural	-40				
South West					
Gloucestershire rural					-960
Somerset rural	-44				
South rural					
Southampton rural	-72				-919
Sussex West rural	-39				
Kent rural					-915
Berkshire rural				-194	-913
Essex rural	-60				-927
South urban					
Southampton urban	-73			-245	-968
Kent urban				-248	-1306
Surrey urban	-147		-22	-441	-2231
Middlesex	165		-29		-1062
Hertfordshire urban	-99		-21	-300	-1199
Essex urban	-87			-351	
London					
Lambeth				735	
Southwark				308	
Hammersmith				706	
Kensington				456	
St. Pancras				297	
Islington				499	

The highest and lowest three figures are shown in dark coloured blocks.

Note: 1. Because mortality is low in children only the highest and lowest five areas are shown.

Table 3 Areas with the ten **highest** and **lowest** excess deaths for females in 1950-53

Area	Infant	Children[1]		Adult	
		1-4	5-14	15-45	45-64
Scotland west and south					
Stirling County			72		
Glasgow City	1392	412	121	4365	6057
Paisley				458	
Lanark County		94	126	815	1186
North East					
Newcastle				408	
Gateshead	270				
Sunderland	249				
Durham urban	543			431	1158
Middlesbrough			75		
Yorkshire urban					
Yorkshire West Riding urban				-158	1014
Hull	281				
Bradford					805
Sheffield		-35			
Lancashire urban					
Lancashire urban	372	95	-36	718	3339
Manchester	446			1283	2494
Liverpool	743	166		1344	1368
West Midlands					
Staffordshire urban	315			339	
Stoke-on-Trent					1045
Birmingham			-41		
Wales					
Cardiganshire rural			72		
Glamorganshire urban	368	149		683	1273
South West					
Bristol	-160				
South rural					
Southampton rural	-89			-131	
Kent rural	-106			-133	-322
Buckinghamshire rural					-330
Norfolk rural					-350
South urban					
Bournemouth					-268
Southampton urban	-125			-147	
Kent urban	-243	-91		-275	-1243
Surrey urban	-365	-50		-541	-1971
Middlesex	-654	-186	-51	-891	-3247
Hertfordshire urban	-134		-30	-205	-542
Essex urban	-349	-85	-39	-471	-1516
London					
Croydon				-129	
Lewisham					-318
Wandsworth	-109				

The highest and lowest three figures are shown in dark coloured blocks.

Note: 1. Because mortality is low in children only the highest and lowest five areas are shown.

Table 4 Areas with the ten **highest** and **lowest** excess deaths for females in 1990-92

Area	Infant	Children[1] 1-4	5-14	Adult 15-45	45-64
Scotland north and east					
Dundee				105	
Edinburgh				246	
Scotland west and south					
Glasgow		56		419	6001
Lanark County					1066
Ayr County				109	792
Wigtown County			59		
North East					
Durham urban					1460
Middlesbrough					773
Lancs/Yorks rural					
Yorkshire West Riding rural			-13	133	
Yorkshire urban					
Yorkshire West Riding urban		-17			
Leeds	83				
Bradford	92		53		
Lancs/Cheshire urban					
Lancashire urban	78	-20			2122
Blackpool		74			
Bolton	85				
Rochdale			48		
Manchester		79		114	1272
Liverpool			49	140	1798
Cheshire urban				-70	
East Midlands					
Derbyshire rural	-43				
Leicester	85				
West Midlands					
Staffordshire urban	131		-18		
Stoke-on-Trent					735
Birmingham	571	114		109	1115
Coventry		63			
Warwickshire rural	85				
Wales					
Glamorganshire urban				-68	
South West					
Somerset urban	-36				
Wiltshire urban			75		
Wiltshire rural				-63	
South rural					
Southampton rural					-625
Kent rural					-577
Berkshire rural	-44				
Buckinghamshire rural				-74	-465
Essex rural					-439
Norfolk rural	-37				-519
South urban					
Southampton urban	-46				-546
Kent urban	-106	-24	-16	-139	
Surrey urban	-77	-15	-13	-153	-1200
Middlesex	-57	-32	-16	-112	-1100
Buckinghamshire urban				-79	
Hertfordshire urban	-80			-121	-600
Essex urban	-92	-15		-228	-641
London					
Lambeth				177	
Bermondsey	77				
Southwark				128	
Islington	113				

The highest and lowest three figures are shown in dark coloured blocks.

Note: 1. Because mortality is low in children only the highest and lowest five areas are shown.

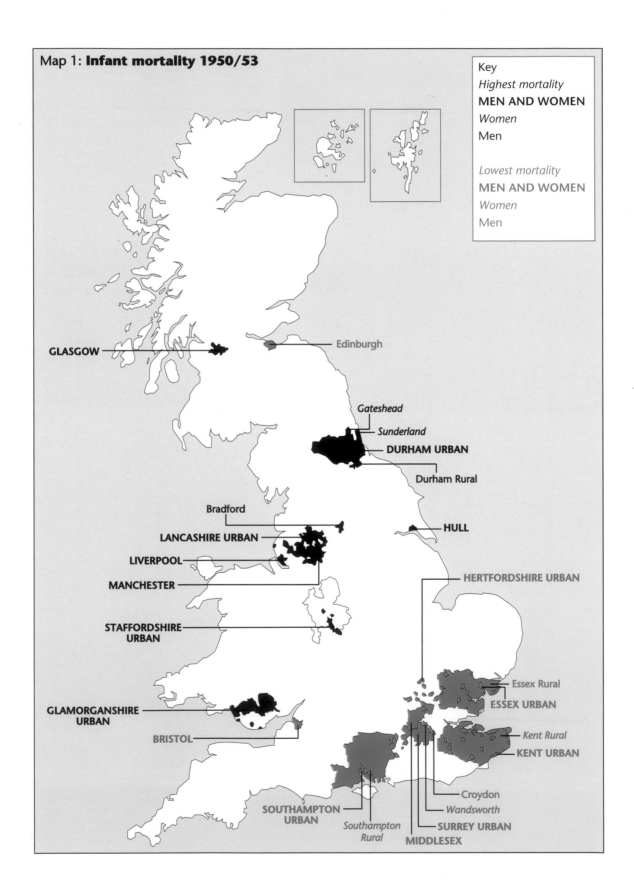

Map 1: **Infant mortality 1950/53**

Key
Highest mortality
MEN AND WOMEN
Women
Men

Lowest mortality
MEN AND WOMEN
Women
Men

GLASGOW

Edinburgh

Gateshead

Sunderland

DURHAM URBAN

Durham Rural

Bradford

HULL

LANCASHIRE URBAN

LIVERPOOL

MANCHESTER

HERTFORDSHIRE URBAN

STAFFORDSHIRE URBAN

Essex Rural

ESSEX URBAN

GLAMORGANSHIRE URBAN

Kent Rural

KENT URBAN

BRISTOL

SOUTHAMPTON URBAN

Southampton Rural

Croydon

Wandsworth

SURREY URBAN

MIDDLESEX

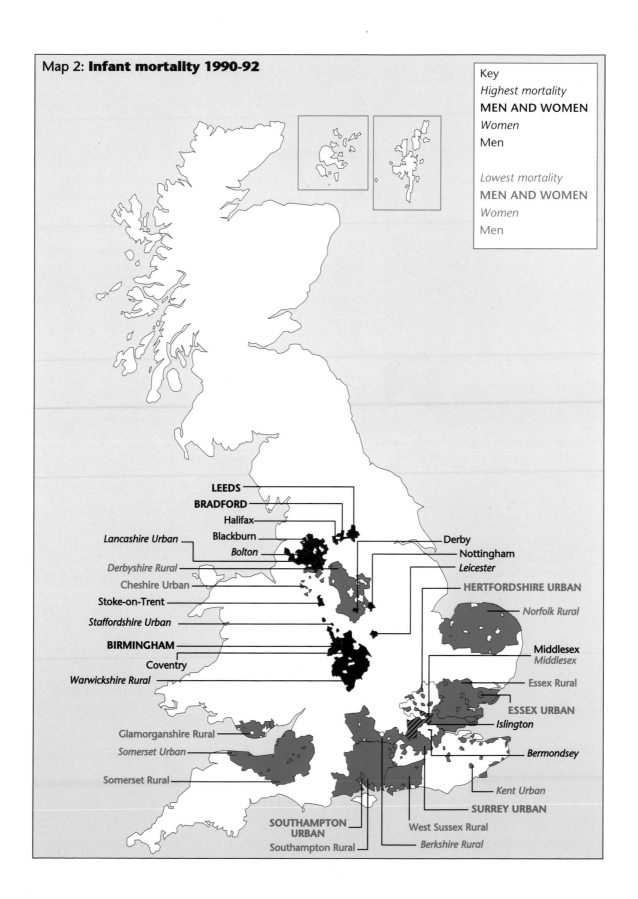

Map 2: **Infant mortality 1990-92**

Key
Highest mortality
MEN AND WOMEN
Women
Men

Lowest mortality
MEN AND WOMEN
Women
Men

LEEDS
BRADFORD
Halifax
Lancashire Urban
Blackburn
Bolton
Derbyshire Rural
Cheshire Urban
Stoke-on-Trent
Staffordshire Urban
BIRMINGHAM
Coventry
Warwickshire Rural

Derby
Nottingham
Leicester
HERTFORDSHIRE URBAN
Norfolk Rural
Middlesex
Middlesex
Essex Rural
ESSEX URBAN
Islington
Bermondsey

Glamorganshire Rural
Somerset Urban
Somerset Rural

Kent Urban
SURREY URBAN

SOUTHAMPTON
URBAN
Southampton Rural
West Sussex Rural
Berkshire Rural

11

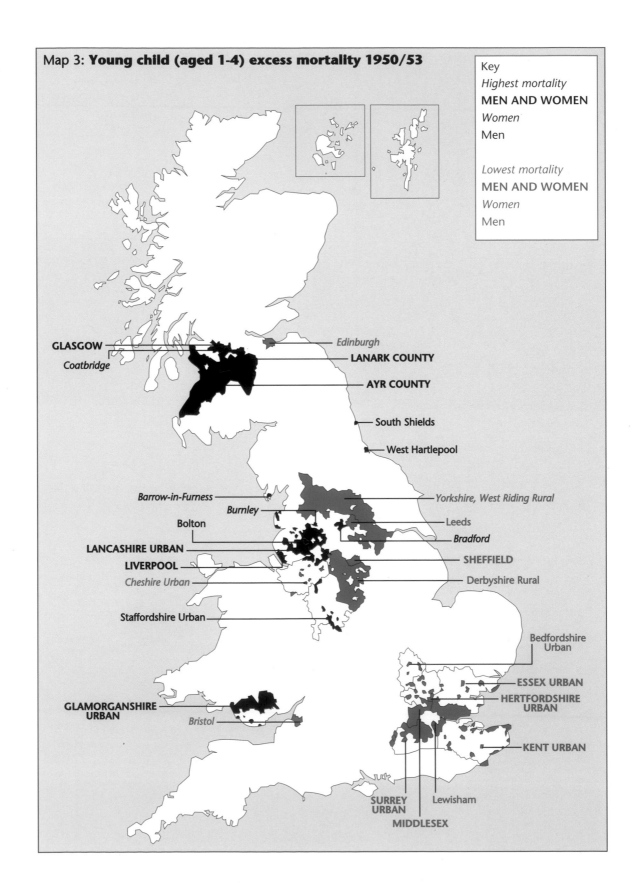

Map 3: **Young child (aged 1-4) excess mortality 1950/53**

Key
Highest mortality
MEN AND WOMEN
Women
Men

Lowest mortality
MEN AND WOMEN
Women
Men

GLASGOW
Coatbridge
Edinburgh
LANARK COUNTY
AYR COUNTY
South Shields
West Hartlepool

Barrow-in-Furness
Yorkshire, West Riding Rural
Burnley
Bolton
Leeds
LANCASHIRE URBAN
Bradford
LIVERPOOL
SHEFFIELD
Cheshire Urban
Derbyshire Rural
Staffordshire Urban

Bedfordshire Urban
ESSEX URBAN
HERTFORDSHIRE URBAN
GLAMORGANSHIRE URBAN
Bristol
KENT URBAN
SURREY URBAN
Lewisham
MIDDLESEX

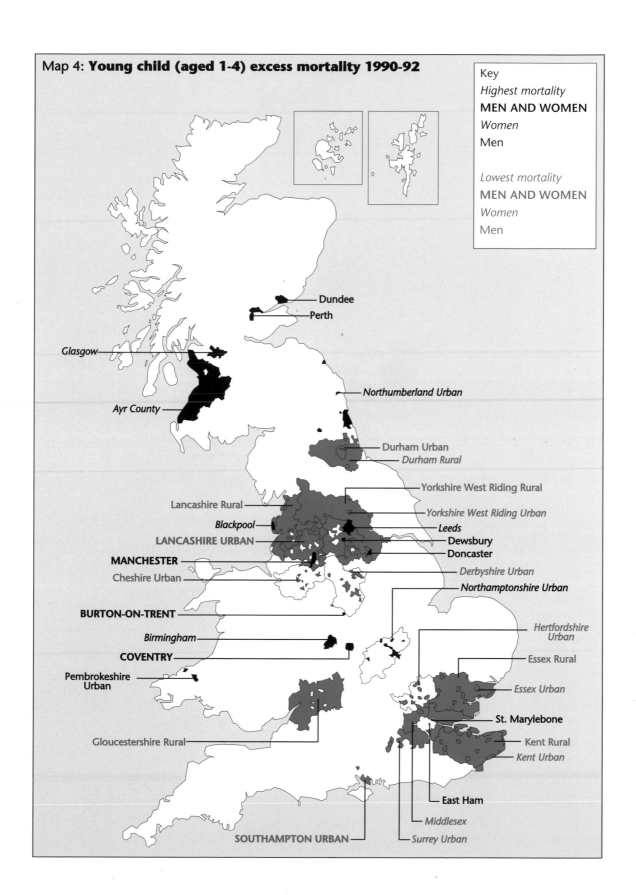

Map 4: **Young child (aged 1-4) excess mortality 1990-92**

Key
Highest mortality
MEN AND WOMEN
Women
Men

Lowest mortality
MEN AND WOMEN
Women
Men

Dundee
Perth
Glasgow
Northumberland Urban
Ayr County
Durham Urban
Durham Rural
Yorkshire West Riding Rural
Lancashire Rural
Yorkshire West Riding Urban
Blackpool
Leeds
LANCASHIRE URBAN
Dewsbury
Doncaster
MANCHESTER
Derbyshire Urban
Cheshire Urban
Northamptonshire Urban
BURTON-ON-TRENT
Hertfordshire Urban
Birmingham
Essex Rural
COVENTRY
Essex Urban
Pembrokeshire Urban
St. Marylebone
Gloucestershire Rural
Kent Rural
Kent Urban
East Ham
Middlesex
SOUTHAMPTON URBAN
Surrey Urban

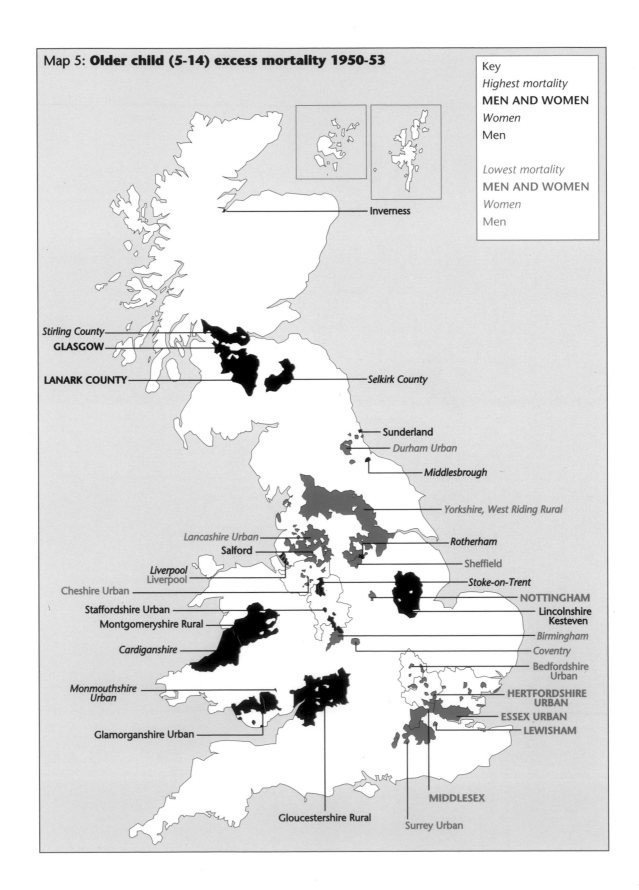

Map 5: **Older child (5-14) excess mortality 1950-53**

Key
Highest mortality
MEN AND WOMEN
Women
Men

Lowest mortality
MEN AND WOMEN
Women
Men

Inverness

Stirling County
GLASGOW
LANARK COUNTY
Selkirk County

Sunderland
Durham Urban
Middlesbrough

Yorkshire, West Riding Rural

Lancashire Urban
Salford
Rotherham
Sheffield

Liverpool
Liverpool
Stoke-on-Trent
Cheshire Urban
NOTTINGHAM
Staffordshire Urban
Lincolnshire Kesteven
Montgomeryshire Rural
Birmingham
Cardiganshire
Coventry
Bedfordshire Urban
Monmouthshire Urban
HERTFORDSHIRE URBAN
ESSEX URBAN
LEWISHAM
Glamorganshire Urban

MIDDLESEX

Gloucestershire Rural
Surrey Urban

Map 6: **Older child (5-14) excess mortality 1990-92**

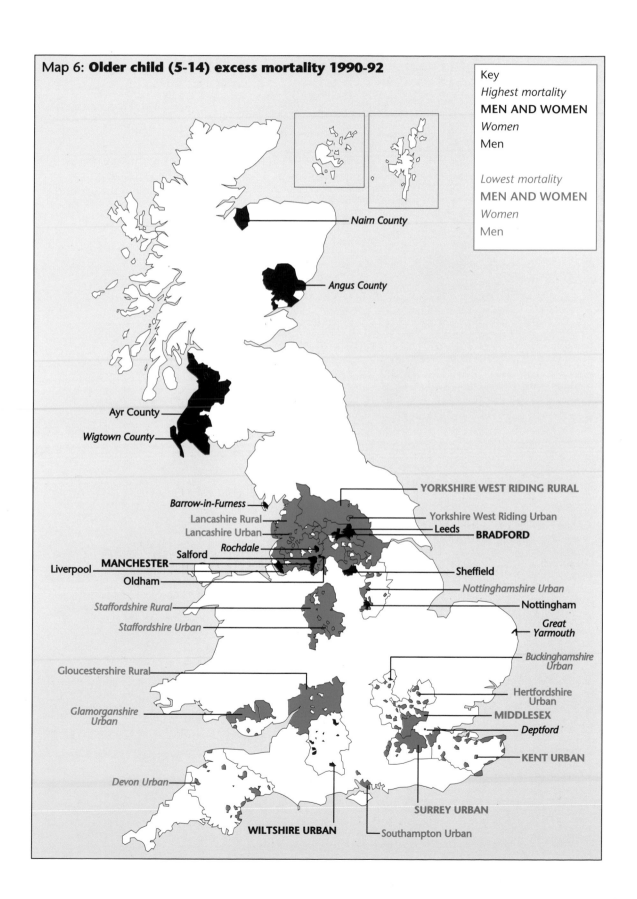

Key
Highest mortality
MEN AND WOMEN
Women
Men

Lowest mortality
MEN AND WOMEN
Women
Men

Nairn County

Angus County

Ayr County

Wigtown County

YORKSHIRE WEST RIDING RURAL

Barrow-in-Furness

Lancashire Rural

Lancashire Urban

Yorkshire West Riding Urban

Leeds

BRADFORD

Rochdale

Salford

Liverpool **MANCHESTER**

Oldham

Sheffield

Nottinghamshire Urban

Nottingham

Staffordshire Rural

Staffordshire Urban

**Great
Yarmouth**

Gloucestershire Rural

*Buckinghamshire
Urban*

Hertfordshire
Urban

*Glamorganshire
Urban*

MIDDLESEX

Deptford

KENT URBAN

Devon Urban

SURREY URBAN

WILTSHIRE URBAN

Southampton Urban

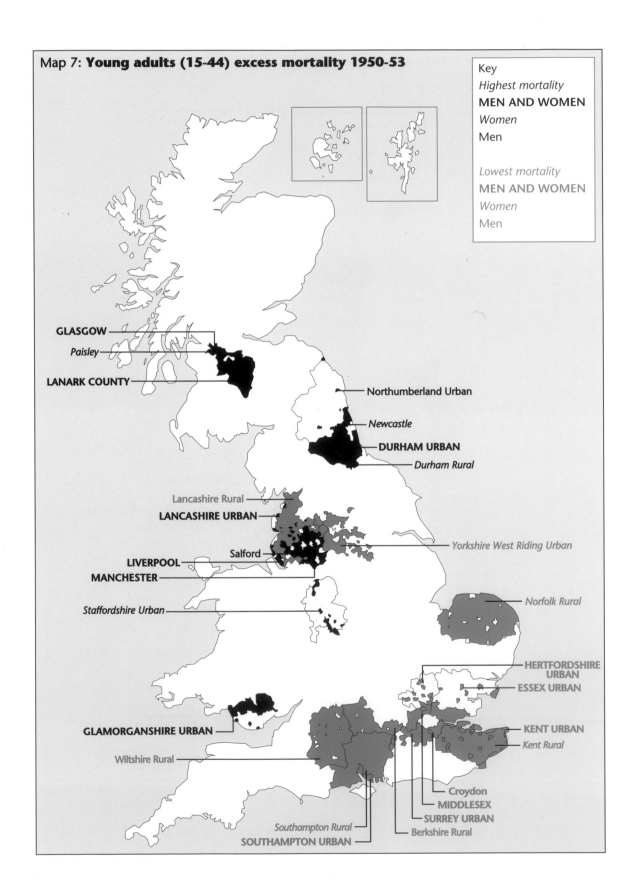

Map 7: **Young adults (15-44) excess mortality 1950-53**

Key
Highest mortality
MEN AND WOMEN
Women
Men

Lowest mortality
MEN AND WOMEN
Women
Men

GLASGOW
Paisley
LANARK COUNTY

Northumberland Urban
Newcastle
DURHAM URBAN
Durham Rural

Lancashire Rural
LANCASHIRE URBAN
Yorkshire West Riding Urban
Salford
LIVERPOOL
MANCHESTER
Staffordshire Urban
Norfolk Rural

HERTFORDSHIRE URBAN
ESSEX URBAN
KENT URBAN
Kent Rural
GLAMORGANSHIRE URBAN
Wiltshire Rural
Croydon
MIDDLESEX
SURREY URBAN
Berkshire Rural
Southampton Rural
SOUTHAMPTON URBAN

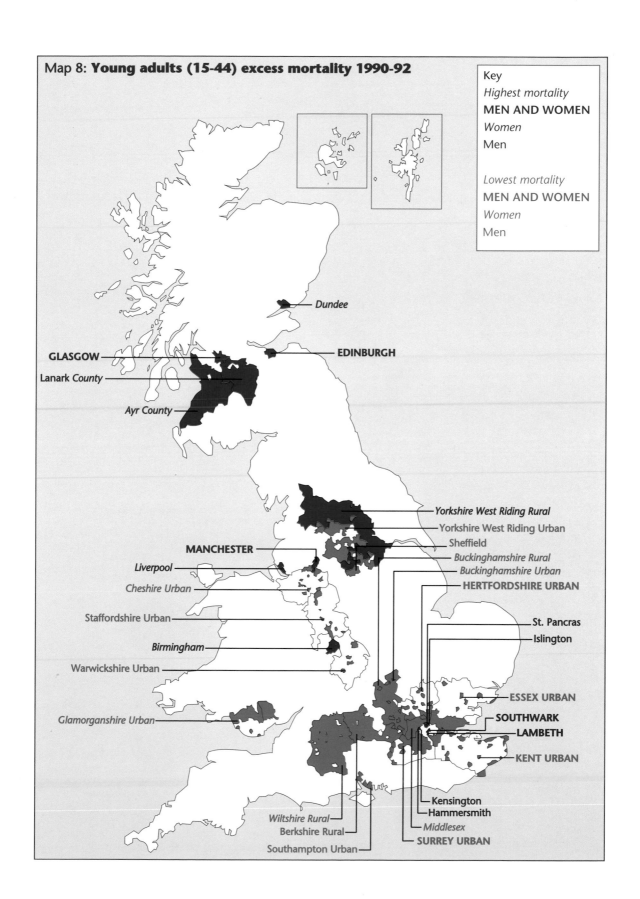

Map 8: **Young adults (15-44) excess mortality 1990-92**

Key
Highest mortality
MEN AND WOMEN
Women
Men

Lowest mortality
MEN AND WOMEN
Women
Men

Dundee

GLASGOW
Lanark County
Ayr County

EDINBURGH

Yorkshire West Riding Rural
Yorkshire West Riding Urban
Sheffield
Buckinghamshire Rural
Buckinghamshire Urban
HERTFORDSHIRE URBAN

MANCHESTER
Liverpool
Cheshire Urban

Staffordshire Urban

St. Pancras
Islington

Birmingham

Warwickshire Urban

ESSEX URBAN

Glamorganshire Urban

SOUTHWARK
LAMBETH

KENT URBAN

Kensington
Hammersmith
Middlesex
SURREY URBAN

Wiltshire Rural
Berkshire Rural
Southampton Urban

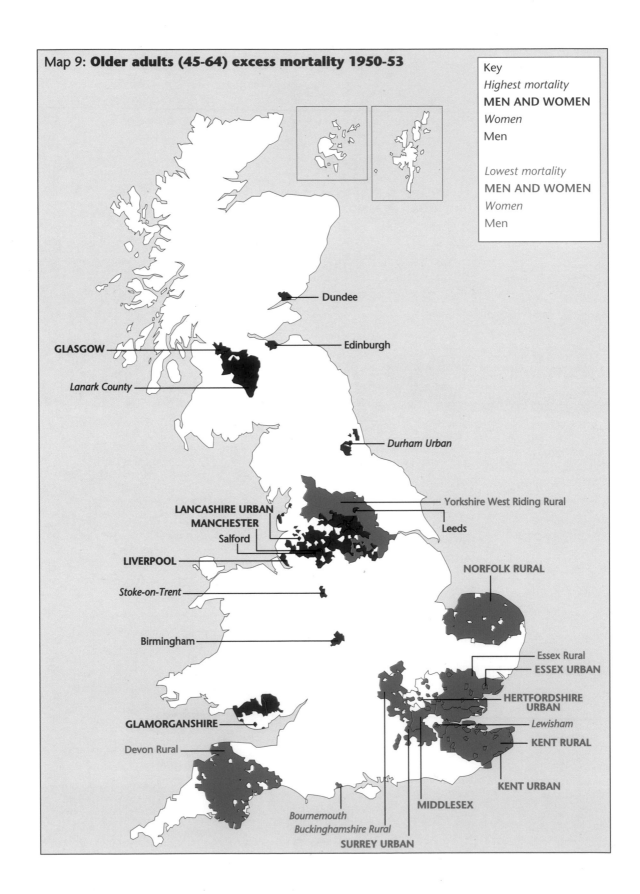

Map 9: **Older adults (45-64) excess mortality 1950-53**

Key
Highest mortality
MEN AND WOMEN
Women
Men

Lowest mortality
MEN AND WOMEN
Women
Men

Dundee

GLASGOW

Lanark County

Edinburgh

Durham Urban

Yorkshire West Riding Rural

LANCASHIRE URBAN
MANCHESTER
Salford

Leeds

LIVERPOOL

Stoke-on-Trent

NORFOLK RURAL

Birmingham

Essex Rural
ESSEX URBAN

HERTFORDSHIRE URBAN

Lewisham

KENT RURAL

GLAMORGANSHIRE

Devon Rural

KENT URBAN

Bournemouth
Buckinghamshire Rural
SURREY URBAN

MIDDLESEX

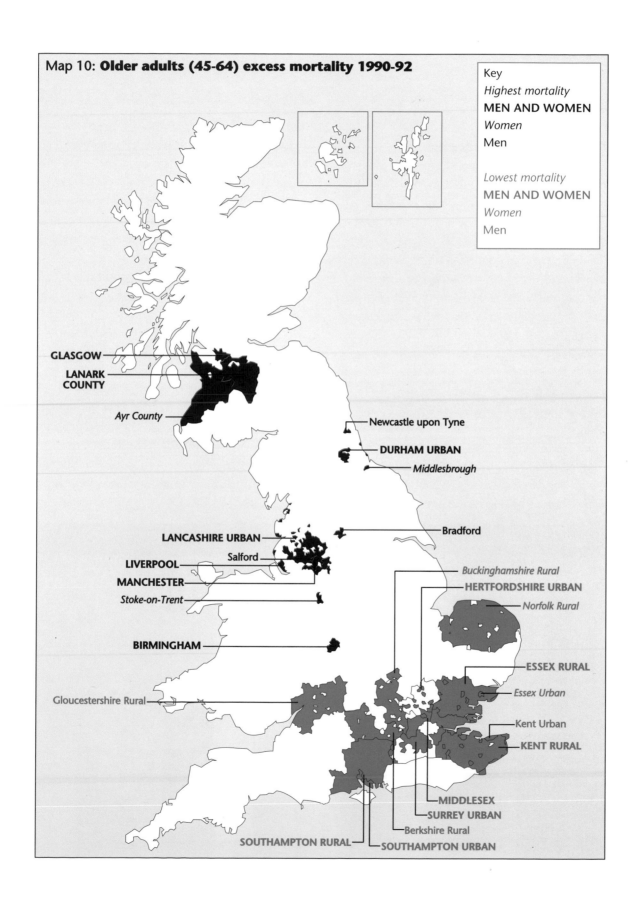

Map 10: **Older adults (45-64) excess mortality 1990-92**

Key
Highest mortality
MEN AND WOMEN
Women
Men

Lowest mortality
MEN AND WOMEN
Women
Men

GLASGOW
LANARK COUNTY
Ayr County
Newcastle upon Tyne
DURHAM URBAN
Middlesbrough
Bradford
LANCASHIRE URBAN
Salford
LIVERPOOL
MANCHESTER
Stoke-on-Trent
BIRMINGHAM
Buckinghamshire Rural
HERTFORDSHIRE URBAN
Norfolk Rural
Gloucestershire Rural
ESSEX RURAL
Essex Urban
Kent Urban
KENT RURAL
MIDDLESEX
SURREY URBAN
Berkshire Rural
SOUTHAMPTON RURAL
SOUTHAMPTON URBAN

2 Overview

Death rates across all ages

Mortality rates are used here to measure the chance of a person dying in a given period. Since World War II, mortality rates have fallen for men, but risen and then fallen for women (see Figure 1). A higher proportion of women now die each year than do men. This trend reflects increases in the number of elderly women in the population. To measure meaningful changes in mortality, either the rates have to be standardised by age structure, or we need to consider separate age and sex groups in turn.

If we standardise the rates to apply to a population with a fixed age structure, then a more informative trend can be seen than the crude death rates (mortality rates not standardised by age or sex) shown in Figure 1. Figure 2 shows how mortality rates have fallen when standardised mortality rates are applied for each period under consideration to the 1951 population of Britain. If the age structure of the population were the same now as it was then, less than 0.9 per cent of men and women would be dying each year given current mortality rates. Because there are now more elderly men and women in the population, current unstandardised mortality rates appear higher.

The fall in mortality over the second half of the twentieth century has been dramatic. The average man is now 30 per cent less likely to die in a given year, and the average woman is 26 per cent less likely to die.

Figure 2 shows the trend for the country as a whole, but it means little in terms of individual life chances. A man aged 55 living in a Bedfordshire town has a chance of dying most similar to that shown in the national

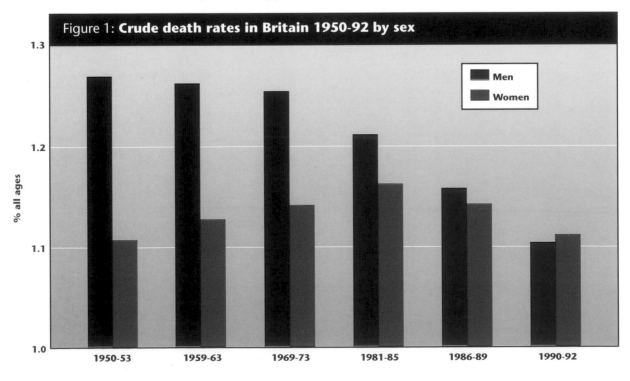

Figure 1: **Crude death rates in Britain 1950-92 by sex**

% all ages

Men
Women

1950-53   1959-63   1969-73   1981-85   1986-89   1990-92 average, represented by the 1990-92 bar of Figure 2, but for most men their life chances are very different. They depend primarily on how old the man is, but are also affected by where he lives, his employment status, his relationships with other people and many other factors. This report concentrates on place and age. In particular, it identifies those groups who have not experienced the general improvement shown above.

By allowing for variations in age structure, standardised mortality ratios can be measured for different areas. These show a person's relative chance of dying each year in an area, accounting for their age or sex. All life chances reported here are relative to the contemporary average mortality rates for all of England and Wales (represented as 100).

Figure 3 shows mortality ratios standardised for age and sex for six places. It illustrates how widely

The ratios in this report have been constructed on a consistent basis using the following age and sex categories to group the population:

infant male (0 years)	infant female (0 years)
child male (1-4 years)	child female (1-4 years)
adolescent male (5-14 years)	adolescent female (5-14 years)
adult male (15-44 years)	adult female (15-44 years)
older male (45-64)	older female (45-64)
male 65 and over	female 65 and over

These are the only groups for which sufficient information was available from past publications; in addition, past official publications only produced results for particular areas for these age groups.

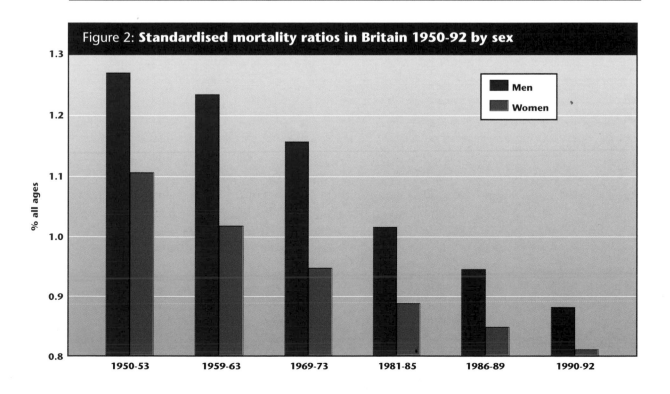

Figure 2: **Standardised mortality ratios in Britain 1950-92 by sex**

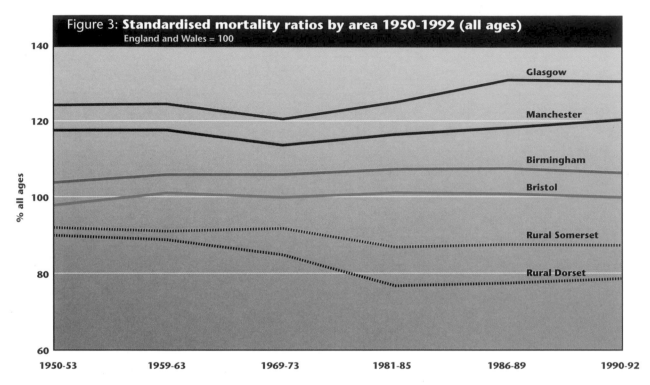

Figure 3: **Standardised mortality ratios by area 1950-1992 (all ages)**
England and Wales = 100

they vary and how little such relative rates tend to change over time. At the end of the 1960s a person living in Glasgow was 42 per cent more likely to die per year than someone living in rural Dorset. By 1992, this 'excess' chance of dying had risen to 66 per cent and 31 per cent more likely than a resident of Bristol. Compared to Bristol, which had a mortality ratio close to the England and Wales average throughout the period, the excess chance of dying rose from 21 per cent to 31 per cent. Crude death rates have fallen for most people in places like Glasgow, but not as quickly as they have in cities further south or in rural areas (where they were also lower to begin with).

Six areas are selected in Figure 3 to highlight the diversity of experience in different parts of Britain throughout the period stated. In the latest period shown, the ratios in the two most extreme of the six areas shown above can be seen to be converging slightly. However, this is not happening everywhere. Maps 11 and 12 (overleaf) show the areas with the highest and lowest standardised mortality ratios in 1950-53 and 1990-92.

Table 5 lists those areas where standardised mortality ratios were above average in the 1981-85 period* and are still rising. It shows how many more people died there in the latest period (1990-92) than the national mortality rates would lead us to expect ('excess deaths'). Here excess deaths are calculated as deaths above the average rate, not deaths above the best rate, which would produce far higher numbers and a much more dramatic summary.

The places listed are among those being left behind by the general improvement in mortality. They only include areas where the ratio has been rising steadily in recent years (unlike Glasgow, which saw a small improvement in the most recent period). The ratios for the early 1950s are included to see how unusual it is for these places to have such high rates relative to the nation as a whole. In the earlier period the 'worst' situation was an increase in the ratio of 3 per decade (Hackney), whereas since the 1980s increases of 7 to 10 per decade have been common, with 3 being the minimum increase among this group of areas.

* The World Health Organization Target One project covers the period 1985 to 2000.

Table 5 **Places where standardised mortality ratios are high and rising in Britain, 1981-92**				
Area	Standardised mortality ratio			Excess deaths
	1950-53	1981-85	1986-89	1990-92	1990-92
Oldham	120	121	124	131	1,102
Salford	121	125	126	131	1,161
Greenock	120	123	127	130	696
Manchester	118	117	119	121	3,390
Birkenhead	112	112	116	121	1,001
Clydebank	112	116	119	120	312
Newcastle upon Tyne	112	112	115	119	1,461
Bolton	117	112	113	118	926
Nairn County	102	109	113	117	76
Liverpool	118	115	116	117	3,033
Falkirk	108	106	116	117	241
Sunderland	112	107	111	117	693
Hackney	99	109	110	116	581
Smethwick	98	103	110	115	249
rural Stirling County	108	109	113	115	755
Southwark	116	103	110	114	250
Edinburgh	109	108	112	114	2,192
Huddersfield	109	110	112	114	646
Bermondsey	104	106	109	114	212
Lambeth	102	110	112	113	632
Zetland County	110	105	107	112	88
Perth Burgh	102	108	111	112	168
rural Durham	108	109	110	111	1,475
Great Yarmouth	102	107	110	111	235
Islington	104	105	106	108	350
rural Perth County	98	102	104	106	240
Plymouth	105	102	103	104	237
Total					**22,400**

There remain areas of this country where, for certain age groups, people's mortality rates are still higher than those experienced by the population as a whole, two or three generations ago. The three areas with the highest mortality rates in the 1990s - Oldham, Salford and Greenock - had mortality ratios nearly a third higher than the national average in the early 1990s, up from about 20 per cent higher in the early 1950s. Nearly 3,000 people who have died in these three areas would still be alive, were the mortality rates not excessive. Even in Plymouth, 237 deaths would not have occurred in 1990-92 had the mortality rates in this town been the same as the average rates for England and Wales as a whole.

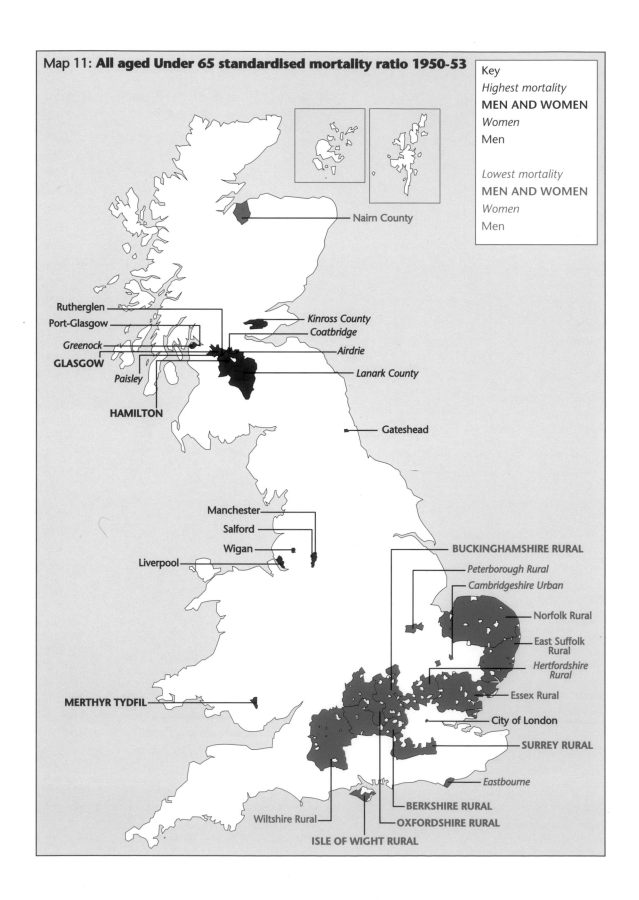

Map 11: **All aged Under 65 standardised mortality ratio 1950-53**

Key
Highest mortality
MEN AND WOMEN
Women
Men

Lowest mortality
MEN AND WOMEN
Women
Men

Nairn County

Rutherglen
Port-Glasgow
Greenock
GLASGOW
Paisley
HAMILTON

Kinross County
Coatbridge
Airdrie
Lanark County

Gateshead

Manchester
Salford
Wigan
Liverpool

BUCKINGHAMSHIRE RURAL
Peterborough Rural
Cambridgeshire Urban
Norfolk Rural
East Suffolk Rural
Hertfordshire Rural
Essex Rural
City of London
SURREY RURAL
Eastbourne

MERTHYR TYDFIL

BERKSHIRE RURAL
OXFORDSHIRE RURAL
Wiltshire Rural
ISLE OF WIGHT RURAL

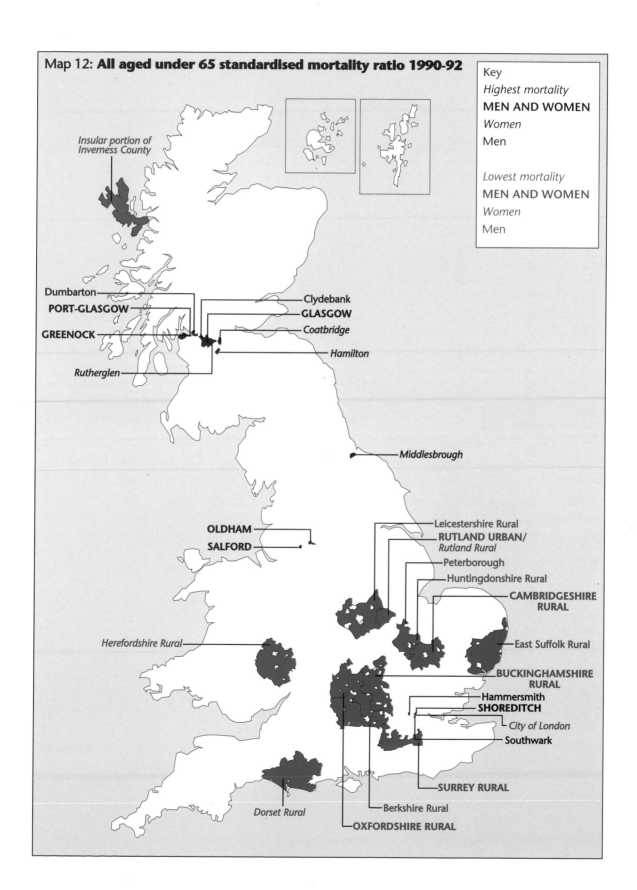

Map 12: **All aged under 65 standardised mortality ratio 1990-92**

Key
Highest mortality
MEN AND WOMEN
Women
Men

Lowest mortality
MEN AND WOMEN
Women
Men

Insular portion of Inverness County

Dumbarton
PORT-GLASGOW
GREENOCK
Rutherglen

Clydebank
GLASGOW
Coatbridge
Hamilton

Middlesbrough

OLDHAM
SALFORD

Leicestershire Rural
RUTLAND URBAN/
Rutland Rural
Peterborough
Huntingdonshire Rural
CAMBRIDGESHIRE RURAL

Herefordshire Rural

East Suffolk Rural
BUCKINGHAMSHIRE RURAL
Hammersmith
SHOREDITCH
City of London
Southwark

Dorset Rural

SURREY RURAL

Berkshire Rural

OXFORDSHIRE RURAL

25

Table 6 **Excess mortality in Britain**

Period	all groups:	men 45 to 64	(change)	women 45 to 64	(change)
1950-53	4.3	7.5		5.6	
1959-63	4.1	6.9	(-0.6)	5.4	(-0.2)
1969-73	4.2	7.1	(+0.2)	6.8	(+1.4)
1981-85	4.2	8.8	(+1.7)	7.8	(+1.0)
1986-89	4.3	9.8	(+1.0)	8.4	(+0.6)
1990-92	4.1	9.6	(-0.2)	8.9	(+0.5)

The total number of excess deaths in the areas given in Table 5 is 22,400. These deaths represent 16 per cent of all mortality in these areas. Nationally there were 77,000 such excess deaths, representing about 4 per cent of all mortality.

Premature deaths

Table 6 shows the total proportion of excess deaths in Britain for each period for which data are available on a consistent basis using identical areas and population groups for each period. Figures are given for the whole population and for the two sub-groups in which most premature deaths occur: men and women aged 45 to 64.

The overall proportion of excess deaths has remained fairly stable over time, at between 4.1 and 4.3 per cent of all deaths. However, for both men and women aged between 45 and 64, the proportion of excess deaths has risen steadily since the early 1970s. In the period 1990-92, the proportion of excess deaths was almost ten per cent for men. The figure for all ages conceals this, because of the large and rising proportion of deaths occurring over the age of 65. Although excess mortality rates for men aged 45 to 64 fell by 0.2 per cent in the most recent years for which comparable data are available, these rates remain very high in historical terms.

Table 7 **Proportion of the population living in areas according to mortality rate**

Period	Standardised mortality ratio 115 plus	95-114	under 95
1950-53	10.3	57.8	31.9
1959-63	7.7	59.8	32.5
1969-73	6.5	60.7	32.8
1981-85	6.6	63.8	29.6
1986-89	8.0	65.0	27.0
1990-92	8.2	65.5	26.4

The proportion of people living in areas of relatively high mortality (with a standardised mortality ratio of 115 or more) fell sharply in the 1950s and 1960s, rose by 0.1 per cent points in the 1970s, by another 1.6 per cent points by the end of the 1980s and by 1990-92 (at 8.2 per cent of the population) was greater than at any time since the mid-1950s (see Table 7). However, at the same time the number of people living in areas with an average life expectancy has grown steadily. This is because the proportion of people living in areas of relatively low mortality has fallen steadily since the end of the 1960s.

In Britain, premature death is becoming more concentrated in certain areas at the same time as it is becoming rarer at young ages. The overall picture is not a simple one: more people are living in areas of average mortality, but more are also living in areas of relatively high mortality; the 1980s have seen a deterioration in equality for many age and sex groups, although for some (such as women aged 45-64) geographical inequality began to increase earlier. Twenty-seven specific areas have experienced a steady relative increase in mortality rates in the 1980s, listed in Table 5, and only three of these areas (Southwark, Liverpool and Plymouth) are now better off than they were in the 1950s when compared to the rest of Britain.

Relatively high death rates in Scotland

Since the mid-1980s, Scotland has shown a particular growth in mortality inequality compared with England and Wales. Between 1950 and 1985 the standard mortality rate for Scotland, relative to England and Wales as 100, never fell below 111 or rose above 112. The rate at which death rates were declining was similar in all three nations. However, since then there have been rapid improvements across England and Wales as a whole, but a lack of rapid improvement in Scotland for those aged over 45.

By 1986-89 the standard mortality rate for Scotland relative to England and Wales had risen to 113, by 1990-92 it was 119 and by 1993-95 it had climbed to 123. The largest increase in the most recent years (for which only figures at the level of the nations making up the UK are available) has been for men aged 45-64 in Scotland, who are now 46 per cent more likely to die per year than their counterparts in England and Wales. Figure 4 includes two age subpopulations of this group (45-54 and 55-64), and illustrates how male mortality rates in Scotland have increased in recent years in relation to England and Wales. It also shows how uniform the rises have been since 1991. For women of these ages the increased likelihood of dying in Scotland is 36 per cent.

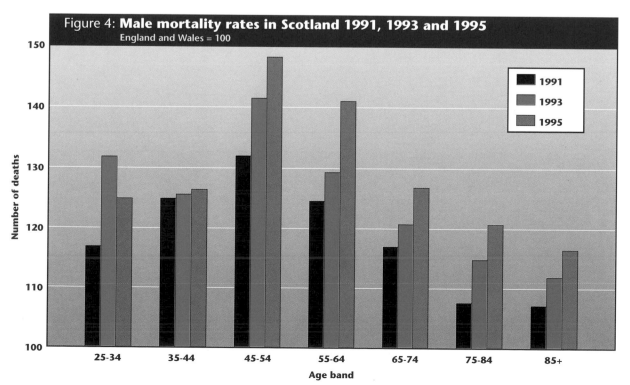

Figure 4: **Male mortality rates in Scotland 1991, 1993 and 1995**
England and Wales = 100

3

Childhood mortality

To be able to locate parts of the country where contemporary mortality rates are actually rising, smaller areas have to be studied than whole countries. To understand whether increases in mortality are real, or simply a statistical artefact, it is best to consider separate age and sex groups of the population, as changes in the relative sizes of these groups can easily alter composite rates. This chapter deals with death rates for groups under the age of 16, and Chapter 4 deals with adult death rates.

The locations chosen for discussion in the following chapters are the most 'consistently divergent' regions in terms of changes in age-specific mortality rates.

Infant mortality

'Infant mortality' refers to death in the first year of life. Of all age groups, infants have experienced the greatest improvement in rates over the period being considered here, although this improvement was most dramatic before 1981. A significant proportion of infants still die in the first year of life (see Figure 5).

Although Figure 5 implies that a plateau in infant mortality rates is being reached, there are still very large variations in rates across the country, which suggests that in those areas with relatively high rates of infant death, there could still be a significant fall. In fact, different areas have experienced very different trends. Figure 6 shows four of the most divergent areas for male infant mortality (from the overall average for England and Wales).

Because of the very low numbers of deaths in this age group, and the low number of infants in the population generally, figures can fluctuate year on year quite widely. However, Figure 6 shows that rates have always been

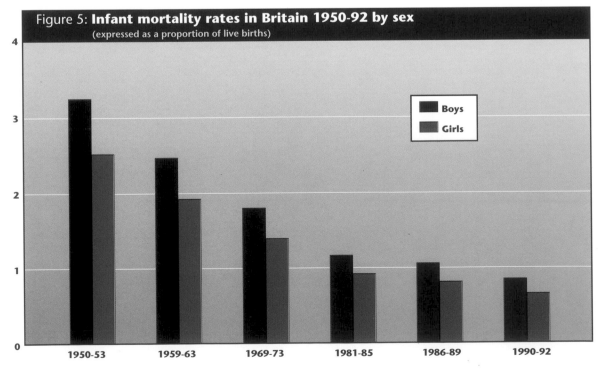

Figure 5: Infant mortality rates in Britain 1950-92 by sex
(expressed as a proportion of live births)

Legend: Boys, Girls

Y-axis: % aged 0 (scale 0 to 4)

X-axis categories: 1950-53, 1959-63, 1969-73, 1981-85, 1986-89, 1990-92

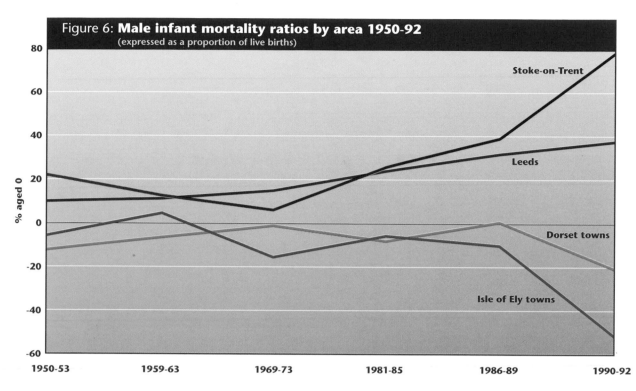

Figure 6: **Male infant mortality ratios by area 1950-92** (expressed as a proportion of live births)

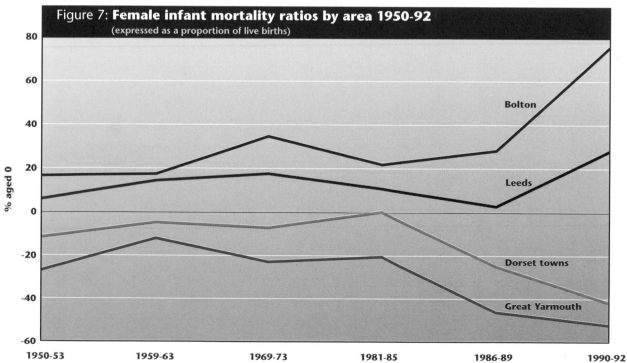

Figure 7: **Female infant mortality ratios by area 1950-92** (expressed as a proportion of live births)

above the national average consistently in places like Leeds and Stoke-on-Trent. The '0 line' represents the average rate for England and Wales.

Currently a high rate of divergence is seen between Stoke and the towns of the old administrative county of Ely (made up of old Wisbech metropolitan borough and the old urban districts of Chatteris, Ely, March and Whittlesey). Male infants in Stoke-on-Trent were more than three times as likely to die in the first year of life than in the Isle of Ely towns, over the latest period for which detailed information is available.

Long-run and persistent trends are more reliable. At the start of the period, infant boys born in Leeds experienced a mortality rate just 10 per cent above the national average. This has risen at every period for which figures are available, and in 1990-92 stood at an excess of 37 per cent over the national average (Figure 6).

A similar group of diverging areas can be found for female infant mortality rates (Figure 7). Again, the overall picture is of a rapid improvement in rates, but this has not been universally distributed. Figure 7 includes two of the areas shown in Figure 6, for comparison. Although infant mortality rates for females in Leeds were converging towards the national rate until recently, the latest figures show the gap to be greater during 1990-92 than at any time since the 1950s, while again rates in Dorset towns are falling much faster than they are nationally.

The net result of these changes is that infant girls in Leeds were, during the period 1990-92, more than twice as likely to die in the first year of life compared with those growing up in Dorset towns (in 1951 the differential was only 20 per cent). Far more dramatic trends can be identified if some of the most extreme places are chosen. For instance, rates between Bolton and Great Yarmouth diverged very widely in the 1980s (Figure 7).

In a few areas, rates have been rising consistently during the 1980s and early 1990s, towards levels that are often twice the national average and in places where rates were around the national average four decades ago. Table 8 lists all those places where infant mortality rates rose in real terms in both the 1980s and into the 1990s.

Area	Infant mortality rate (%)				Change (%)
	1950-53	1981-85	1986-89	1990-92	1981-92
For males					
Britain	3.25	1.15	1.04	0.81	-30
Blackburn	3.45	1.35	1.36	1.78	32
Halifax	3.80	1.25	1.51	1.54	23
Preston	3.51	1.17	1.27	1.47	26
Southwark	2.44	1.21	1.36	1.40	15
For females					
Britain	2.53	0.89	0.78	0.62	-30
Paisley	2.91	0.95	1.12	1.17	23

Table 8 **Places where infant mortality rates are high and rising in Britain 1981-92 (aged 0)**

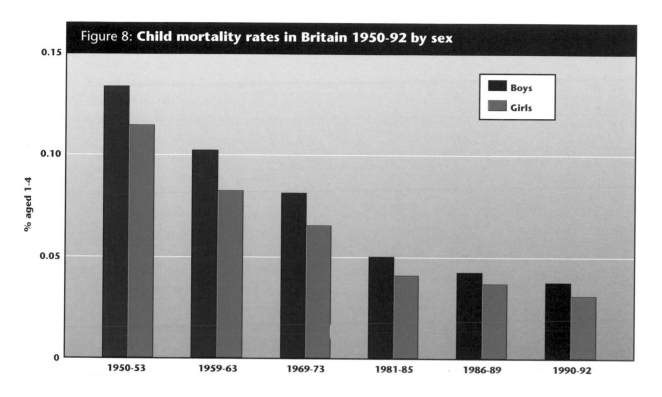

Figure 8: **Child mortality rates in Britain 1950-92 by sex**

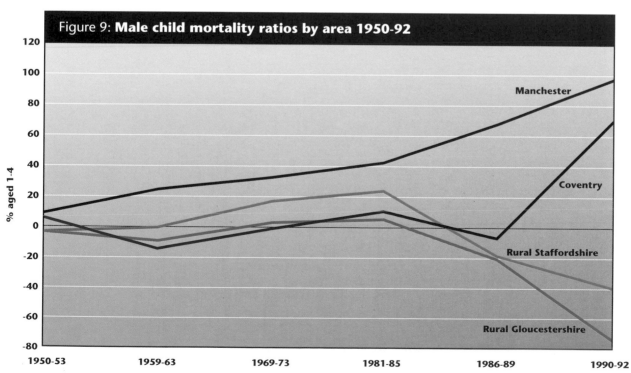

Figure 9: **Male child mortality ratios by area 1950-92**

When the current differences are compared with past rates, the increase in the gap can be seen to be stark. Southwark's results are notable; it had below average male infant mortality rates in the early 1950s, but by 1992 rates were approaching twice the national average. (Figures for Holborn borough have not been included in Table 8 because several children's hospitals are located there. Very poorly infants, who survive the first six months of life but then die, may have their place of death assigned to medical facilities located in Holborn.)

Childhood mortality

Childhood mortality is death at between ages 1 to 4, and is identified separately from infant mortality because there are often very different causes of death. This is also one of the narrowest age bands for which mortality rates can be compared, by area, with the past. (Unfortunately, for older groups, large age ranges are often amalgamated in past published records.) Nationally, mortality rates for children age 1 to 4 are much lower than for infants, but have

fallen at a similar rate, to stabilise in the early 1980s (Figure 8). Although the age group is four times bigger than for infants, the number of deaths in this group is much smaller and so figures for individual places and small periods can vary even more over short periods of time.

Figure 9 shows a group of areas which have seen very different trends over recent years, and compares those trends with the past, when the four areas had quite similar rates.

Male child mortality rates have increased steadily in Manchester, in relation to the country as a whole, while in the rural districts of Gloucestershire they have fallen very quickly in recent years. The gap between these two places is such that, proportionally, almost eight times more male infants died in Manchester in the 1990-92 period, than in rural Gloucestershire, but it must be remembered that these are some of the most extreme figures and that rates for this small group can vary greatly year on year (as is illustrated by recent

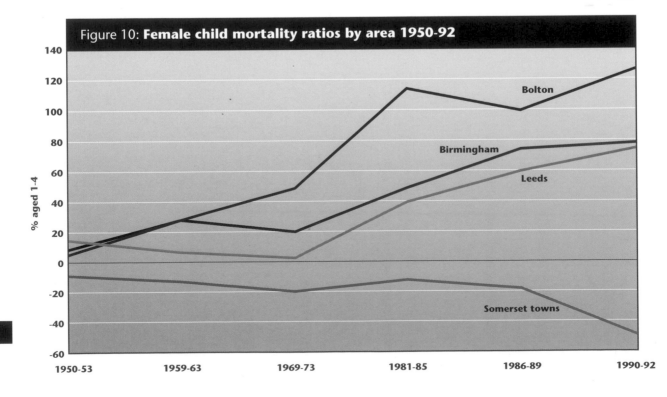

Figure 10: **Female child mortality ratios by area 1950-92**

trends in Coventry, shown in Figure 8). Nevertheless, at the start of this period none of these areas had male childhood mortality rates that varied by as much as 10 per cent from the national rate. By the end of the period they varied from twice the national rate, to almost a quarter of it.

A similar picture can be painted by looking at areas which show diverging trends for mortality among female children (Figure 10). The large cities of Bolton, Birmingham and Leeds have also experienced relative increases in female mortality rates since the end of the 1960s, whereas mortality rates in areas like the towns of Somerset are currently falling more rapidly than the national average, despite already (and consistently) being lower than that rate.

Comparing Bolton and the Somerset towns, the differences between mortality rates for this age and sex group are now more than fourfold, while in the major cities of Leeds and Birmingham mortality rates for this group are now more than 70 per cent above the national average. However, these are not the most extreme examples; they are shown in Table 9.

Table 9 lists all areas where rates have risen in real terms since 1981, and which were already above the national average. Manchester appears in the figures for both males and females. Child mortality rates in Manchester in 1950 were very similar to the national rate then. Although they have fallen to half that rate, the national rate fell to under a third of its 1950s level over the same period. Most dramatic, perhaps, is Bethnal Green, where the mortality rate for males aged 1 to 4 was, in 1990-92, higher than it was in 1950. Again, the caveat about the

Table 9 Places where child mortality rates are high and rising in Britain, 1981-92 (aged 1 to 4)

| Area | Child mortality rate (%) | | | | Change (%) |
	1950-53	1981-85	1986-89	1990-92	1981-92
For males					
Britain	0.14	0.05	0.04	0.04	-25.00
Dewsbury	0.12	0.05	0.08	0.11	108.33
Bethnal Green	0.10	0.06	0.06	0.11	81.03
St. Helens	0.17	0.05	0.06	0.07	43.32
Manchester	0.15	0.07	0.07	0.08	4.37
For females					
Britain	0.12	0.04	0.04	0.03	-24.94
rural Isle of Wight	0.09	0.04	0.05	0.06	45.83
Chelsea	0.13	0.04	0.05	0.06	44.23
Manchester	0.12	0.05	0.06	0.06	33.37
Birkenhead	0.14	0.05	0.06	0.06	32.31
Newport	0.10	0.05	0.05	0.05	9.00

the fastest falls, for many different groups of the population, does not occur by chance.

Figure 13 uses the same scale as Figure 12. There is less variation in mortality for women, and hence the picture is less divergent. However, it is still the case that when comparing two northern cities, and in this case two rural areas, there is usually divergence in recent years. It is worth pointing out that at no time in the last half century were the rates in the rural areas higher than those in the cities shown here, despite the fluctuations in rates based on such small numbers of deaths.

Again it is worth stressing that mortality rates for this age group are very low and falling nationally. Only a very few areas have seen consistent rises in absolute mortality rates (number of deaths divided by people at risk) to high levels for these groups over the 1980s for boys, and only one area for girls (where the rise may be caused by very few deaths). These areas are shown in Table 10, and are compared to the national decline.

The largest rise, seen in Salford, still leaves its mortality rate almost half that of the area in the early 1950s, whereas in Nottingham and Bethnal Green rises in mortality amongst boys have brought the levels to approach those of the early 1950s (where they were then below average). In all these areas, rates in the early 1980s were very similar to the national average. It has been changes during the 1980s which have led to the divergence seen across the country.

Similar places to those in Table 9 can again be seen. For example, Table 9 showed that in Bethnal Green male childhood mortality had been rising during the 1980s to a point where it was higher than in the 1950s. Male *adolescent* mortality is also unusually high in Bethnal Green, and rising steadily (by 30 per cent in real terms from 1981 to 1992). The reappearance of the same places and regions in this report provides the strongest evidence of systematic polarisation.

Table 10 **Places where adolescent mortality rates are high and rising in Britain, 1981-92 (age 5 to 14)**

Area	Adolescent mortality rate (%)				Change (%)
	1950-53	1981-85	1986-89	1990-92	1981-92
For males					
Britain	0.06	0.03	0.02	0.02	-21.18
Salford	0.09	0.03	0.04	0.05	50.93
rural Camarthenshire	0.06	0.03	0.04	0.04	50.62
St. Helens	0.06	0.03	0.04	0.04	21.88
Nottingham	0.04	0.03	0.04	0.04	33.85
Bethnal Green	0.04	0.03	0.03	0.03	30.10
For females					
Britain	0.04	0.02	0.01	0.01	-19.32
Barrow-in-Furness	0.02	0.02	0.02	0.05	148.96

trends in Coventry, shown in Figure 8). Nevertheless, at the start of this period none of these areas had male childhood mortality rates that varied by as much as 10 per cent from the national rate. By the end of the period they varied from twice the national rate, to almost a quarter of it.

A similar picture can be painted by looking at areas which show diverging trends for mortality among female children (Figure 10). The large cities of Bolton, Birmingham and Leeds have also experienced relative increases in female mortality rates since the end of the 1960s, whereas mortality rates in areas like the towns of Somerset are currently falling more rapidly than the national average, despite already (and consistently) being lower than that rate.

Comparing Bolton and the Somerset towns, the differences between mortality rates for this age and sex group are now more than fourfold, while in the major cities of Leeds and Birmingham mortality rates for this group are now more than 70 per cent above the national average. However, these are not the most extreme examples; they are shown in Table 9.

Table 9 lists all areas where rates have risen in real terms since 1981, and which were already above the national average. Manchester appears in the figures for both males and females. Child mortality rates in Manchester in 1950 were very similar to the national rate then. Although they have fallen to half that rate, the national rate fell to under a third of its 1950s level over the same period. Most dramatic, perhaps, is Bethnal Green, where the mortality rate for males aged 1 to 4 was, in 1990-92, higher than it was in 1950. Again, the caveat about the

Table 9 **Places where child mortality rates are high and rising in Britain, 1981-92 (aged 1 to 4)**

Area	Child mortality rate (%)				Change (%)
	1950-53	1981-85	1986-89	1990-92	1981-92
For males					
Britain	0.14	0.05	0.04	0.04	-25.00
Dewsbury	0.12	0.05	0.08	0.11	108.33
Bethnal Green	0.10	0.06	0.06	0.11	81.03
St. Helens	0.17	0.05	0.06	0.07	43.32
Manchester	0.15	0.07	0.07	0.08	4.37
For females					
Britain	0.12	0.04	0.04	0.03	-24.94
rural Isle of Wight	0.09	0.04	0.05	0.06	45.83
Chelsea	0.13	0.04	0.05	0.06	44.23
Manchester	0.12	0.05	0.06	0.06	33.37
Birkenhead	0.14	0.05	0.06	0.06	32.31
Newport	0.10	0.05	0.05	0.05	9.00

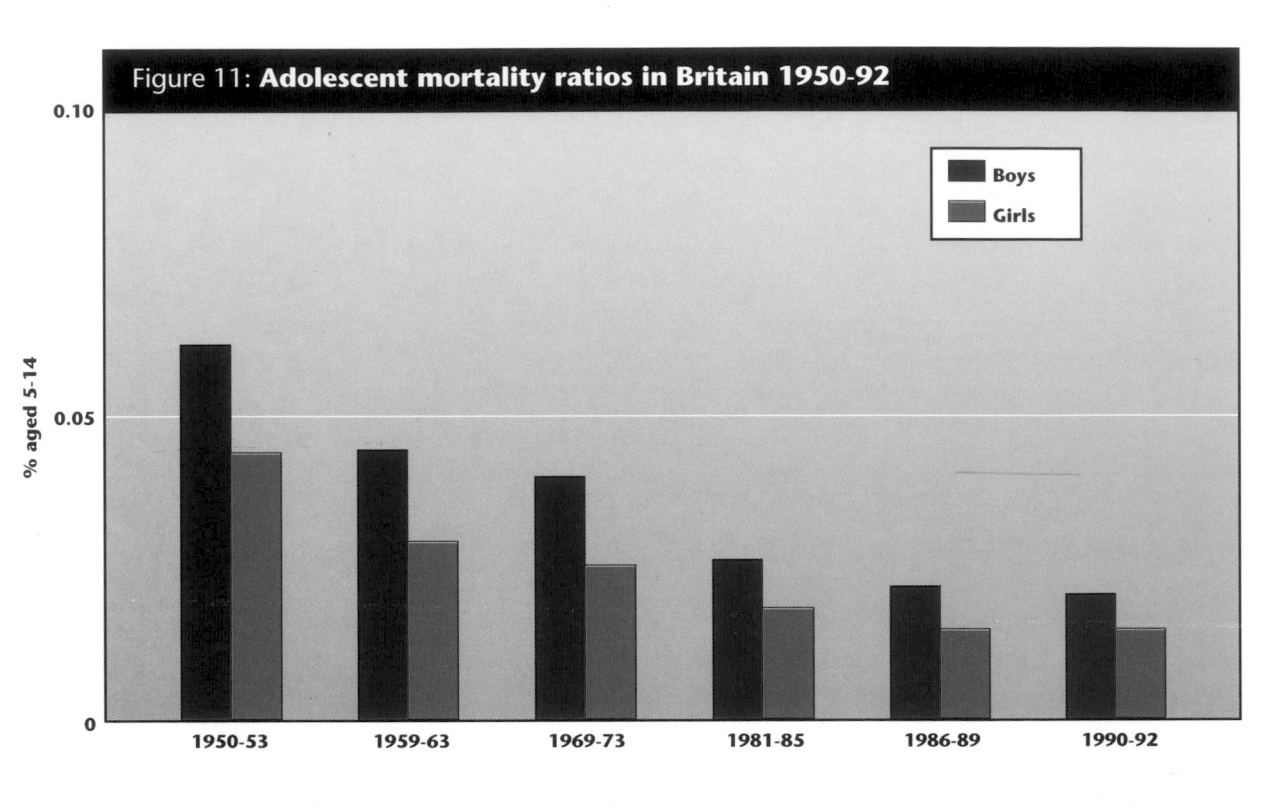

Figure 11: **Adolescent mortality ratios in Britain 1950-92**

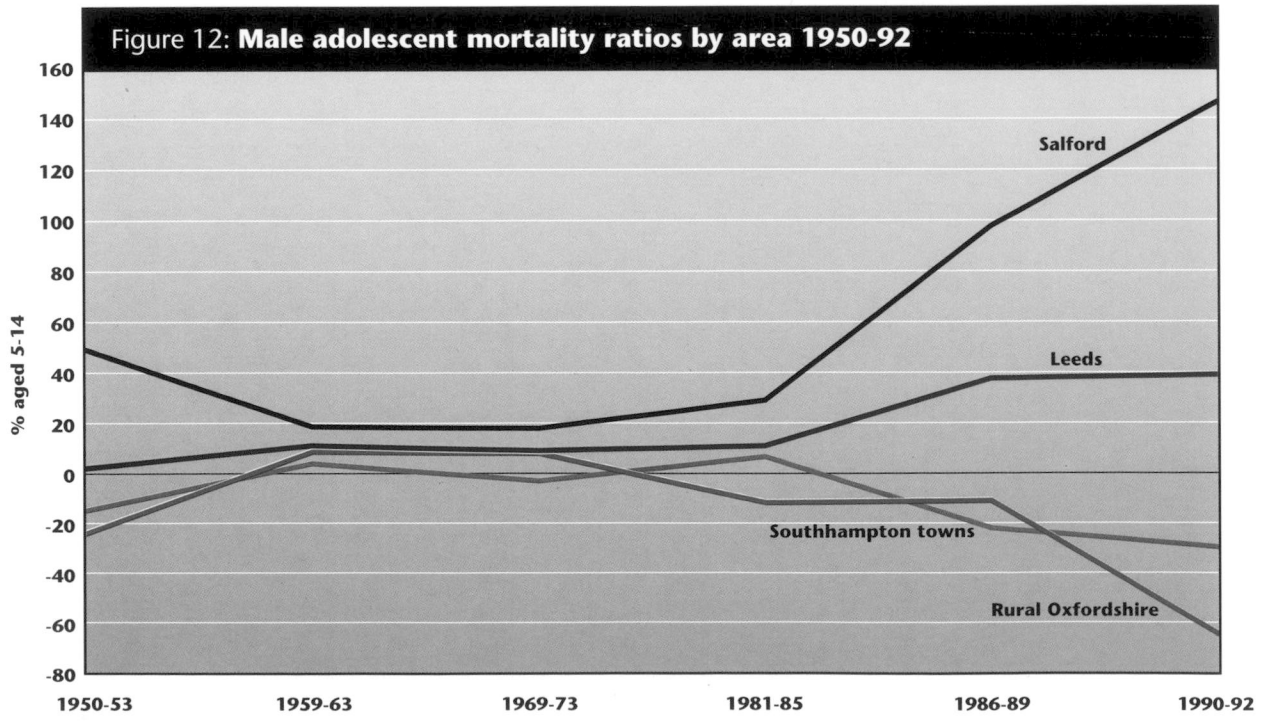

Figure 12: **Male adolescent mortality ratios by area 1950-92**

trends in Coventry, shown in Figure 8). Nevertheless, at the start of this period none of these areas had male childhood mortality rates that varied by as much as 10 per cent from the national rate. By the end of the period they varied from twice the national rate, to almost a quarter of it.

A similar picture can be painted by looking at areas which show diverging trends for mortality among female children (Figure 10). The large cities of Bolton, Birmingham and Leeds have also experienced relative increases in female mortality rates since the end of the 1960s, whereas mortality rates in areas like the towns of Somerset are currently falling more rapidly than the national average, despite already (and consistently) being lower than that rate.

Comparing Bolton and the Somerset towns, the differences between mortality rates for this age and sex group are now more than fourfold, while in the major cities of Leeds and Birmingham mortality rates for this group are now more than 70 per cent above the national average. However, these are not the most extreme examples; they are shown in Table 9.

Table 9 lists all areas where rates have risen in real terms since 1981, and which were already above the national average. Manchester appears in the figures for both males and females. Child mortality rates in Manchester in 1950 were very similar to the national rate then. Although they have fallen to half that rate, the national rate fell to under a third of its 1950s level over the same period. Most dramatic, perhaps, is Bethnal Green, where the mortality rate for males aged 1 to 4 was, in 1990-92, higher than it was in 1950. Again, the caveat about the

Table 9 Places where child mortality rates are high and rising in Britain, 1981-92 (aged 1 to 4)

Area	Child mortality rate (%)				Change (%)
	1950-53	1981-85	1986-89	1990-92	1981-92
For males					
Britain	0.14	0.05	0.04	0.04	-25.00
Dewsbury	0.12	0.05	0.08	0.11	108.33
Bethnal Green	0.10	0.06	0.06	0.11	81.03
St. Helens	0.17	0.05	0.06	0.07	43.32
Manchester	0.15	0.07	0.07	0.08	4.37
For females					
Britain	0.12	0.04	0.04	0.03	-24.94
rural Isle of Wight	0.09	0.04	0.05	0.06	45.83
Chelsea	0.13	0.04	0.05	0.06	44.23
Manchester	0.12	0.05	0.06	0.06	33.37
Birkenhead	0.14	0.05	0.06	0.06	32.31
Newport	0.10	0.05	0.05	0.05	9.00

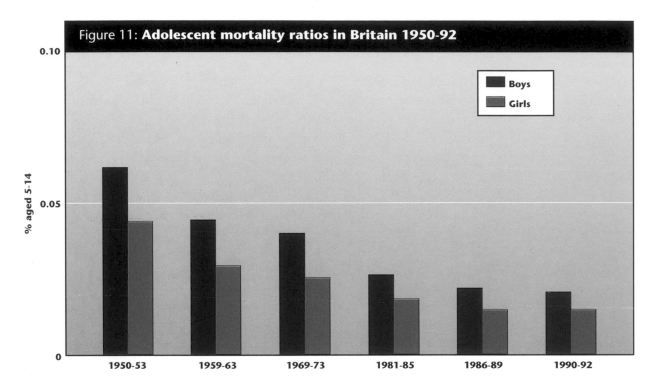

Figure 11: **Adolescent mortality ratios in Britain 1950-92**

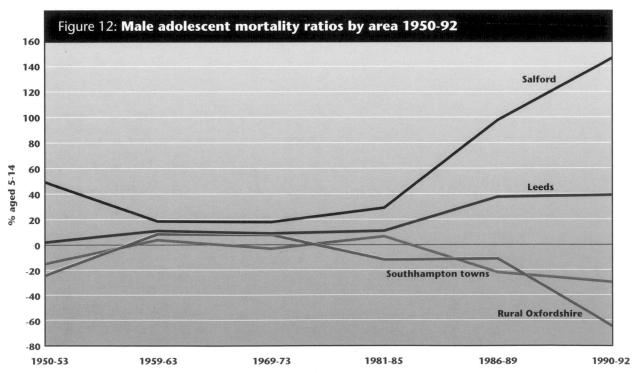

Figure 12: **Male adolescent mortality ratios by area 1950-92**

presence of child medical facilities apply, but it is difficult to see how these could affect only one sex for Bethnal Green.

Adolescent mortality

Adolescent mortality is death at between ages 5 and 14. It too has been falling steadily in Britain over the period of study (Figure 11). This is the age group for which mortality is least common. By the early 1990s less than one girl in every seven thousand in this age group was dying per year. It is therefore important to realise that the graphs and tables here are based on relatively few deaths.

Because the overall mortality rates are very low, some of the widest divergent trends in mortality can be found for this group by area. Figure 12 shows four places which all had quite similar adolescent mortality rates for boys (of around the national average) between 1959 and 1985. Since then the two northern areas have seen

their rates rise rapidly in the period to 1992, fastest in the smaller area, while the two southern areas have seen rates fall over the same period. As a result, by the early 1990s, boys in Salford were seven times more likely to die than those living in rural Oxfordshire, whereas thirty years earlier the difference had been only 8 per cent. Although these figures alone are not utterly reliable, they are indicative of the types of changes which are worth investigation. The divergence for the two larger areas (Leeds and Southampton), where a few percent points difference has grown into a twofold difference, is similarly interesting if less extreme.

The areas being shown in these graphs are often extreme or steadily divergent cases, but they are indicative of some of the general trends that are occurring in mortality rates across the country as overall rates fall. The repetition of northern towns showing absolute and relative rises and southern (and particularly rural) areas showing

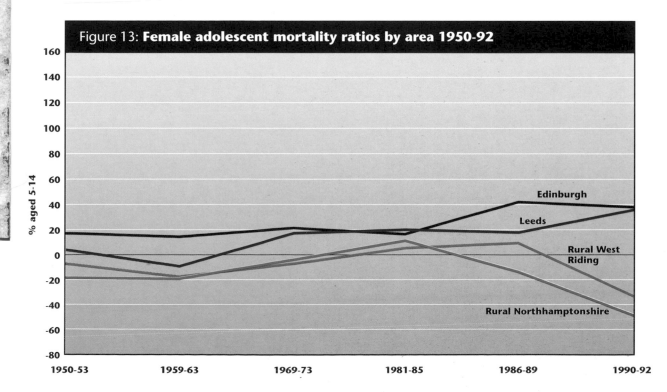

Figure 13: **Female adolescent mortality ratios by area 1950-92**

the fastest falls, for many different groups of the population, does not occur by chance.

Figure 13 uses the same scale as Figure 12. There is less variation in mortality for women, and hence the picture is less divergent. However, it is still the case that when comparing two northern cities, and in this case two rural areas, there is usually divergence in recent years. It is worth pointing out that at no time in the last half century were the rates in the rural areas higher than those in the cities shown here, despite the fluctuations in rates based on such small numbers of deaths.

Again it is worth stressing that mortality rates for this age group are very low and falling nationally. Only a very few areas have seen consistent rises in absolute mortality rates (number of deaths divided by people at risk) to high levels for these groups over the 1980s for boys, and only one area for girls (where the rise may be caused by very few deaths). These areas are shown in Table 10, and are compared to the national decline.

The largest rise, seen in Salford, still leaves its mortality rate almost half that of the area in the early 1950s, whereas in Nottingham and Bethnal Green rises in mortality amongst boys have brought the levels to approach those of the early 1950s (where they were then below average). In all these areas, rates in the early 1980s were very similar to the national average. It has been changes during the 1980s which have led to the divergence seen across the country.

Similar places to those in Table 9 can again be seen. For example, Table 9 showed that in Bethnal Green male childhood mortality had been rising during the 1980s to a point where it was higher than in the 1950s. Male *adolescent* mortality is also unusually high in Bethnal Green, and rising steadily (by 30 per cent in real terms from 1981 to 1992). The reappearance of the same places and regions in this report provides the strongest evidence of systematic polarisation.

Table 10 **Places where adolescent mortality rates are high and rising in Britain, 1981-92 (age 5 to 14)**

Area	Adolescent mortality rate (%)				Change (%)
	1950-53	1981-85	1986-89	1990-92	1981-92
For males					
Britain	0.06	0.03	0.02	0.02	-21.18
Salford	0.09	0.03	0.04	0.05	50.93
rural Camarthenshire	0.06	0.03	0.04	0.04	50.62
St. Helens	0.06	0.03	0.04	0.04	21.88
Nottingham	0.04	0.03	0.04	0.04	33.85
Bethnal Green	0.04	0.03	0.03	0.03	30.10
For females					
Britain	0.04	0.02	0.01	0.01	-19.32
Barrow-in-Furness	0.02	0.02	0.02	0.05	148.96

4

Adult mortality

Younger adults

Because this report is constrained to looking at the age groups for which figures were published in the 1950s and 1960s, the 15 to 44 year age range is considered as a single group, classified as young adults. One advantage of looking at such a large group is that the number of deaths being considered is quite significant, and so concerns about short-term fluctuations are much less important here.

The picture nationally is very similar as that for children, with rates falling fastest in the first three decades after World War II (Figure 14). There is one very important difference, however - the death rate for young adult men, unlike all other groups, has not fallen throughout the 1980s; in fact their chances of

dying have risen sharply when compared to women of the same age. Young adult men used to be 28 per cent more likely to die than women at the start of the period; they are now 89 per cent more likely to die in a given year:

Because the absolute mortality rate for men has been stable nationally, the changes by area are particularly simple to interpret. Many parts of the country have seen a gradual improvement, but a large minority of areas have seen rates rise in real terms. Figure 15 highlights four areas that typify this divergence. In Surrey towns and rural Berkshire, mortality rates for men fell over the 1980s as a whole. In contrast, rates in place like Southwark and Oldham have risen sharply. In the period 1950-53, a young adult man in Southwark was 47 per cent more likely

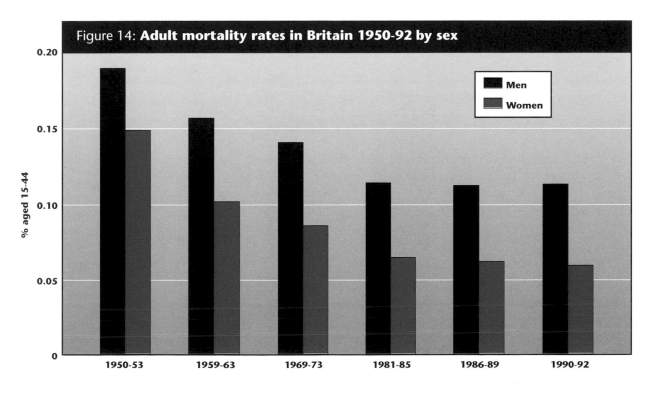

Figure 14: **Adult mortality rates in Britain 1950-92 by sex**

to die than one in rural Surrey; by 1990-92, the differential had grown to 164 per cent.

This is a divergence of particular concern because it involves so many deaths, and the areas undergoing rising mortality rates are widespread as compared to the areas with rising absolute childhood mortality rates. The

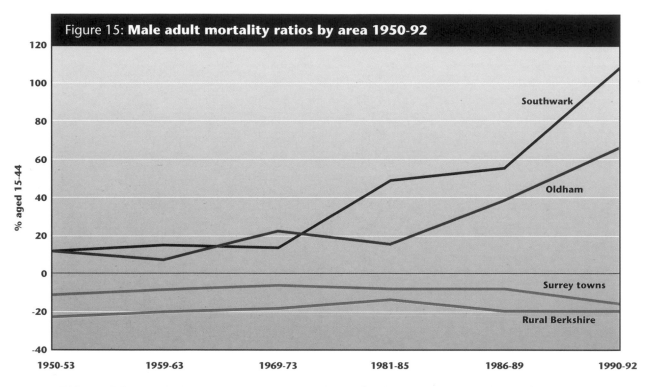

Figure 15: **Male adult mortality ratios by area 1950-92**

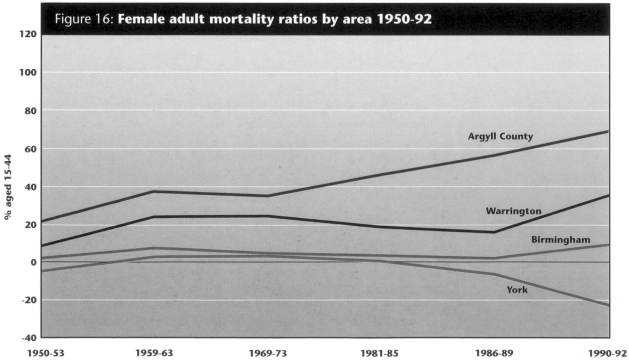

Figure 16: **Female adult mortality ratios by area 1950-92**

divergence also appears to be increasing over time, particularly rapidly in recent years, and with no indication that it is slowing down.

Nationally, mortality rates for men aged 15 to 44 rose by 3 per cent between 1993 and 1995; rates for women in this period were stable, so the divergence does appear to be continuing.

Young adult mortality rates for women show a similar pattern to those for men, but with less extreme differences (Figure 16). Argyll County and Warrington, two areas which traditionally had above average death rates, are worsening, particularly in comparison to York, where female young adult mortality rates fell during the 1980s. For many parts of the country, typified by Birmingham, there has been little change over the period 1950-92.

Table 11 lists all the places where young adult mortality rates were higher than the national average at the start of the 1980s and where rates have risen since, ranked by how high the rates are now.

The City of London ranks highest, but is a very small area. Nevertheless, a higher proportion of young adult men are dying there now every year than just after World War II. The same is true of the old London Boroughs of Hammersmith, Islington, Southwark, Lambeth, Kensington and Bermondsey. Elsewhere, the largest increases for this group in the 1980s (all over 20 per cent in real terms) were found in Port-Glasgow, Oldham, Halifax, Brighton, Burnley, Hamilton, Dundee and Edinburgh.

All the places listed should raise concern, and be subject to further investigation. What has changed about the lives of men in these place to increase the number of deaths in these age groups so substantially? No single cause or

explanation is likely to be adequate to explain all of the excess deaths in an area, let alone the increases across so many areas.

In the three-year period around the 1991 census, well over 1,500 more men aged between 15 and 44 died than would have died had mortality rates remained unchanged in their area since 1981. The geographical distribution of all the places with more than ten additional deaths for males in this age group is as follows:

More than 50:
    Middlesex (104), Edinburgh (74),
    Hammersmith (57), Bristol (56)
40 to 50:
    Glasgow (49), Essex towns (43),
    Brighton (43)
30 to 40:
    Birkenhead (37), Lewisham (37),
    rural Lanark County (35), Kensington (35),
    Oldham (32), Islington (31), Lambeth (31),
    rural Lancashire (31)
20 to 30:
    Dundee (29), Leicestershire towns (29),
    Wallasey (29), Manchester (26),
    Oxfordshire towns (26), Wiltshire towns
    (26), Woolwich (25), Grimsby (25),
    Hertfordshire towns (24), Southwark (24),
    Halifax (24), East Ham (23), Cheshire towns
    (23), East Sussex towns (23), West Sussex
    towns (23), Norfolk towns (21),
    Bournemouth (21), Southampton (21),
    Hackney (20)
10 to 20:
    Burnley (18), rural Glamorganshire (18),
    Bermondsey (16), Barrow-in-Furness (16),
    Durham towns (16), rural Gloucestershire
    (16), Isle of Wight towns (15), Clydebank (15),
    Worcestershire towns (15), rural
    Northamptonshire (14), Norwich (14),
    Warrington (14), Bolton (14), rural Dorset

Table 11 **Places where adult mortality rates are high and rising in Britain, 1981-92**

Area	Adult mortality rate (%)				Change(%)
	1950-53	1981-85	1986-89	1990-92	1981-92
For males					
Britain	0.19	0.11	0.11	0.11	-1.40
City of London	0.19	0.24	0.25	0.32	32.88
Hammersmith	0.17	0.17	0.20	0.26	55.23
Port-Glasgow	0.30	0.15	0.16	0.24	61.07
Southwark	0.21	0.17	0.18	0.24	38.70
Lambeth	0.18	0.18	0.20	0.20	12.33
Kensington	0.18	0.16	0.16	0.20	23.08
Islington	0.16	0.16	0.17	0.19	15.84
Glasgow	0.27	0.18	0.18	0.19	6.19
Oldham	0.21	0.13	0.16	0.19	41.95
Bermondsey	0.18	0.13	0.16	0.18	35.68
Burnley	0.23	0.14	0.14	0.18	30.65
Camberwell	0.18	0.15	0.16	0.17	8.10
Halifax	0.23	0.12	0.15	0.17	32.98
Dundee	0.24	0.13	0.14	0.16	21.36
Preston	0.23	0.14	0.14	0.16	13.83
Hackney	0.18	0.14	0.15	0.16	14.08
Brighton	0.19	0.12	0.15	0.16	31.78
Poplar	0.20	0.14	0.15	0.15	9.02
Hamilton	0.26	0.12	0.14	0.15	25.41
Edinburgh	0.22	0.12	0.13	0.15	20.72
West Ham	0.19	0.13	0.13	0.14	3.79
Cumberland towns	0.25	0.13	0.13	0.14	7.57
Battersea	0.18	0.12	0.13	0.13	11.75
Barnsley	0.20	0.12	0.12	0.13	15.20
Denbighshire towns	0.21	0.12	0.12	0.12	6.41
North Riding towns	0.21	0.12	0.12	0.12	4.40
For females					
Britain	0.15	0.07	0.06	0.06	-8.00
Roxburgh County	0.16	0.08	0.08	0.11	42.76
Kinross County	0.28	0.08	0.09	0.10	19.60
Argyll County	0.18	0.09	0.10	0.10	6.49
Ross & Cromarty County	0.19	0.08	0.09	0.10	26.21
Hamilton	0.23	0.07	0.08	0.09	31.43
rural Herefordshire	0.14	0.07	0.08	0.08	22.06
Derby	0.12	0.07	0.07	0.07	10.76

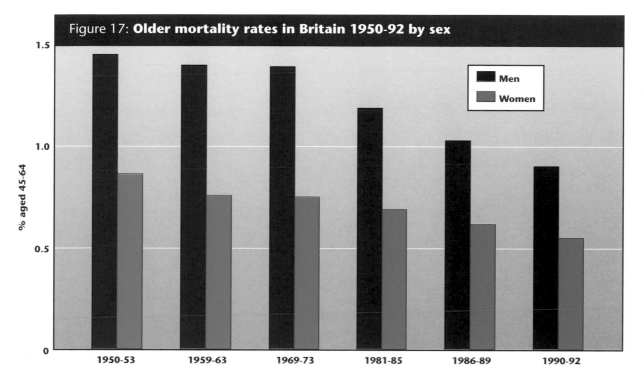

Figure 17: **Older mortality rates in Britain 1950-92 by sex**

(13), Hampstead (13), St Pancras (13), Camberwell (12), Yorkshire, East Riding towns (12), Port-Glasgow (12), rural Essex (12), Bradford (11), Battersea (11), West Suffolk towns (10), Preston (10), rural Cheshire (10), rural Westmorland (10) and Croydon (10).

Although some of these numbers may appear low, it must be remembered that these are the deaths *in excess* of the number that would be expected amongst an age group in which death is normally rarely expected. These are also only figures for a relatively short period of time - many more excess deaths in this age group can be expected to have occurred in these areas since the figures were collected. Finally, the death of a young adult is likely to have a very wide impact on the local community.

The places in Table 11 are ranked according to the absolute mortality rates of men and women in the latest period. Only places which had a higher rate than the national average at the start of the 1980s are shown, and then only places where the absolute rates have been rising are included. Despite these constraints, the list is long.

The lack of concordance between places where young men and women are increasingly likely to die is interesting. By early young adulthood the causes of deaths of men and women tend to be quite different. For women, no particularly dramatic divergent trends can be seen (although the inclusion of so many rural Scottish counties is intriguing). It is for men of these ages that most questions need to be asked.

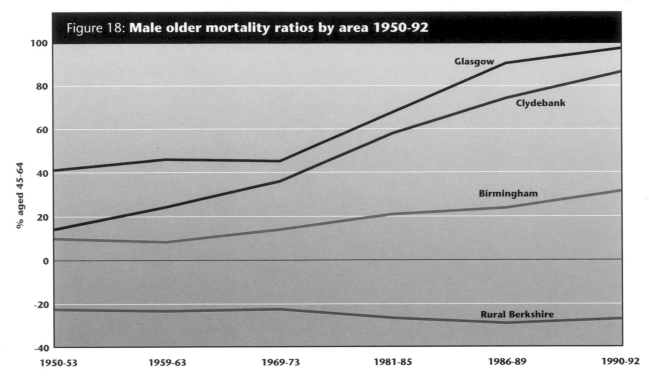

Figure 18: **Male older mortality ratios by area 1950-92**

Older mortality

Changes in mortality for the next oldest age group show a very different trend to that for younger adults. The improvement in mortality for men aged between 45 and 64 has mainly occurred since the 1980s, resulting in a narrowing of the gap between men's and women's life chances in this age group (Figure 17). However, men's chances are still much higher than women's, with just under one per cent of men in this age group dying per year, and just over half a per cent of women dying per year. Whatever their sex, mortality is of greater concern to people of these ages, because the chances are much higher than for younger adults.

Areas can be selected which show a clear divergence in mortality rates. For men, two urban areas of Scotland have been selected where relative rates have risen quite rapidly (Figure 18). These contrast with Birmingham which has seen slower, but continued, relative increases, and rural Berkshire, where older male

mortality rates have always been more than 20 per cent below the national average.

In Glasgow alone over 1,000 men aged 45 to 64 die per year, 1.74 per cent of the population at risk. If the rate there was the same as the national average for men (0.91 per cent) then almost half these men would not die until they were at least 65 years old. Over a three-year period, the decrease in numbers of excess deaths in Glasgow would almost equal the numbers of excess deaths just discussed, in terms of younger men nationally, such is the increase in mortality rates with age. This is why spatial inequalities at these ages are very important, despite being less extreme in terms of percentages (Figure 18).

In national terms there has also been a divergence in rates at older ages, particularly in the most recent years. In 1991 men aged 45 to 64 in Scotland were 27 per cent more likely to die than their counterparts in England and

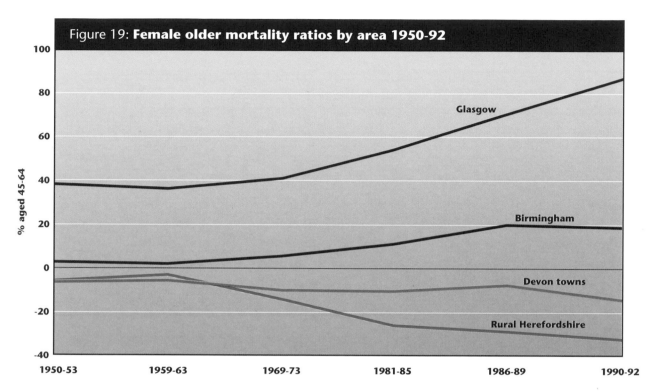

Figure 19: **Female older mortality ratios by area 1950-92**

Wales. By 1995 the differential had risen to 46 per cent - a rapid (and continuous) change in a five-year period. For women the proportion of excess deaths increased from 26 per cent in 1991, to 36 per cent in 1995.

For women, Glasgow shows a similar trajectory to that seen for men (Figure 19), whereas deaths in Birmingham have stopped rising in relative terms over the most recent period. Two areas in the south of England are included in the graph to show how different the trajectories of areas with relatively good health can be.

Although there are many areas of interest in terms of relative divergences in mortality rates for this age group, only one area had a rate higher than the national average in the 1981 to 1985 period which has risen steadily since then. This is Shoreditch (for men) and it is included in Table 12 for consistency. Note how nationally there has been a rapid fall in mortality amongst older men, with almost a quarter less dying by the start of the 1990s as compared with the start of the 1980s. Against this background of rapidly falling rates it is surprising to even find one area where rates have consistently risen in recent years.

Table 12 **Places where older mortality rates are high and rising in Britain 1981-92**

Area	Older mortality rate (%)				Change (%)
	1950-53	1981-85	1986-89	1990-92	1981-92
For males					
Britain	1.46	1.19	1.03	0.91	-23.67
Shoreditch	1.85	1.45	1.54	1.71	17.63

A tale of two cities

This short report has presented a mixed picture with several recurrent themes. Against a background of general national improvement in mortality rates, particular areas and particular groups can be seen to be faring less well. Two large cities at opposite ends of Britain - Glasgow and Bristol - can be used to summarise many of the findings of this research:

1   Nationally, mortality rates for all groups have fallen by 28 per cent between 1950 and 1992. They fell by 23 per cent in Glasgow and 27 per cent in Bristol (applying current age-sex specific rates to the 1950-53 population of each city).

2   Geographical inequalities are often wider than these falls. Between 1990 and 1992 a resident of Glasgow was 31 per cent more likely to die than a resident of Bristol. Between 1950 and 1953 that difference was 27 per cent.

3   People in Glasgow aged between 15 and 64 had a higher mortality rate in the early 1990s than did people of the same age when they were living in Bristol in the early 1950s.

4   Glasgow and Bristol are not untypical: nationally, 8.2 per cent of people live in high mortality areas like Glasgow (the highest proportion since the 1950s), and Bristol's overall mortality rate mirrors the national average.

5   There are large, and in many cases widening, differences in life chances across Britain. In many areas, adults today are experiencing worse mortality rates than many adults living in other areas experienced just after World War II.

6   Young adult men experience the widest inequalities in life chances. One man in 540 aged between 15 and 44 in Glasgow died each year in 1990-92, 43 per cent more per person at risk than in Bristol in 1990-92.

7   Over one hundred more men aged 15 to 44 died in Bristol and Glasgow combined between 1990 and 1992 than would have died had the mortality rates not risen in those cities for this age group since 1981.

8   If mortality rates for men aged 15 to 44 in Glasgow were reduced to the national average for 1990-92, one hundred male deaths a year would be delayed in that city alone (and 30 deaths of women of these ages).

9   If mortality rates for men aged 45 to 64 in Glasgow were reduced to the national average for 1990-92, five hundred deaths a year would be delayed in Glasgow (and seventy deaths of women of these ages).

10 Until long-standing mortality inequalities in places like Glasgow are broken and new trends such as rising deaths of young men in affluent cities such as Bristol are reversed, Britain will fail to attain Target One of the World Health Organization. There is no evidence of reductions in inequalities in mortality occurring in Britain.

Bristol and Glasgow have been used as convenient large cities to illustrate the general spatial trends in life-chances in Britain over the course of the last half century. Bristol could have been compared with the rural populations of a large Home County and similar figures on differences produced, only then mortality in Bristol would have been perceived as being unreasonably high.

This report has not taken the usual approach (which is adopted with social class differentials), and asked why mortality rates cannot be the same as in the 'best' places. Instead, places have been compared with the national average for England and Wales. Altering this base does not change the conclusions, but would make the results less comparable with other reports. This report has also only examined six broad age groups; wider differentials can be found if more groups are examined. Similarly, only large areas have been studied to maintain historical continuity. If small areas, such as wards, are examined for trends in the 1980s alone, then much wider divisions are found.

Conclusion: inequalities by area

The account presented above concentrates largely on examples of the worst and best cases and does not look at the overall picture (although excess mortality in Britain is given in Tables 6 and 7). To get a feel for the overall position, it is helpful to divide the population into ten equal-size population groups, known as decile groups. The 'bottom' group is made up of the worst tenth of areas in terms of high mortality ratios for those aged below 65, the next group is the second-worst tenth, and so on up to the best tenth of areas, which have the lowest standardised mortality ratio for the under-65 population. These decile groups can then be compared, and the relative changes in their mortality charted over time.

The under-65 standardised mortality ratios are used because it is also important to concentrate on the deaths which are most avoidable in society and most costly to it (which mainly occur before retirement age). The places comprising each decile of the population can thus change over time as the relative health of areas change.

Table 13 shows the absolute mortality rate in each decile over the study period. Even without allowing for population structure, it is evident that by the end of the period the mortality rate of those aged under 65 living in the worst decile area, at 3.25 per thousand, is more than 66 per cent higher than that in the best. This inequality is 43 per cent greater than it was in the early 1960s and the death rate in the worst areas is higher than that experienced by people living in the best area twenty years earlier (3.07 per thousand). There has clearly been no convergence in mortality rates between these equal sized groups of the population.

Table 13 Absolute mortality rate per 1,000 of the population at risk aged under 65 by decile area

Population decile	1950-53	1959-63	1969-73	1981-85	1986-89	1990-92
1	5.72	5.20	5.01	4.10	3.61	3.25
2	5.22	4.86	4.46	3.58	3.20	2.89
3	5.13	4.52	4.30	3.48	3.05	2.68
4	4.71	4.49	4.06	3.31	2.88	2.56
5	4.64	4.25	3.96	3.12	2.73	2.45
6	4.46	4.08	3.72	2.93	2.62	2.27
7	4.17	3.73	3.58	2.79	2.45	2.27
8	4.01	3.82	3.41	2.68	2.44	2.19
9	3.86	3.70	3.31	2.60	2.29	2.05
10	3.68	3.64	3.07	2.38	2.15	1.94

Table 14 **Age and sex standardised mortality ratio for deaths at ages under 65 by decile area**

Population decile	1950-53	1959-63	1969-73	1981-85	1986-89	1990-92
1	131.0	135.5	131.2	135.0	139.2	142.3
2	118.1	123.0	115.6	118.6	120.9	121.4
3	112.1	116.5	112.0	114.2	113.9	111.3
4	107.0	110.7	108.1	109.8	106.9	104.9
5	102.5	104.5	103.0	102.1	102.2	99.0
6	98.6	97.4	96.9	95.7	95.6	93.5
7	93.1	90.9	91.8	91.6	91.9	90.9
8	88.7	87.6	88.9	89.3	89.1	86.5
9	85.7	83.1	87.0	84.3	83.0	80.4
10	81.8	77.1	83.0	79.2	78.1	76.2

When the mortality rates are corrected to allow for the differences in the population structure of each group, the divergence in mortality rates by area becomes even more clear (Table 14). The 10 per cent of people living in the areas of the country with the highest death rates have the worst ever recorded relative mortality rates in the most recent period, with a standardised mortality rate of 142.3. Since 1981 the standardised mortality ratio of this group has risen by 7.4 percentage points, and that of the second decile of the population has risen by 2.7 percentage points. All other decile groups have seen their relative mortality rates fall over this period. When standardised for age and sex distributions, people living in the worst areas of Britain in 1990-92 were 42.3 per cent more likely to die before age 65 than the average person, while people in the best decile area were 23.8 per cent less likely to die. The gap has grown greatly since the 1950s when those in the worst areas were only 31 per cent more likely to die than average, while people in the best areas were only 18.2 per cent less likely to die before the age of 65.

Many of the trends which have been shown here have occurred too quickly, or involve too many deaths, to be ascribed simply to changing socio-economic structures, or changing causes of deaths, or simply the reflection of past health variations. Explaining the patterns of life chances will be far more difficult than describing them. The areas listed in Table 15 constitute the population living in places with the highest premature mortality ratios in the early 1990s. The table also shows the total numbers of people who died before age 65 in each area, between 1990 and 1992.

Mortality and poverty

It can be seen from Table 16 that the areas which are the poorest deciles in terms of health are also the poorest in terms of affluence on a number of indicators. People are four times more likely to have no access to a car in the highest mortality decile than the lowest. Similarly, their children are four times more likely to be living in a household without work. Adults aged under 65 in these areas are twice as likely to suffer from illness.

Table 15 **Age, sex standardised mortality ratio for deaths at ages under 65 by decile area, 1990-92**

Rank	Area	SMR<65	deaths	Rank	Area	SMR<65	deaths
1	Glasgow County of City	179	6,489	27	Blackburn	136	728
2	Shoreditch	169	184	28	Stirling Burgh	135	264
3	Greenock Burgh	168	552	29	St Pancras	135	701
4	Salford	166	834	30	Liverpool	135	3,836
5	Port-Glasgow Burgh	166	206	31	Paisley Burgh	135	673
6	Clydebank Burgh	163	367	32	Burnley	135	554
7	Oldham	157	789	33	Dundee County of City	135	1,328
8	Southwark	155	433	34	Bethnal Green	134	205
9	Middlesbrough	154	1,031	35	Finsbury	134	151
10	Coatbridge Burgh	153	439	36	Wallasey	133	707
11	Dumbarton Burgh	148	197	37	Bolton	131	1,024
12	Manchester	147	3,567	38	Birkenhead	131	948
13	Lambeth	147	1,400	39	Bradford	131	2,034
14	Hammersmith	147	633	40	Camberwell	130	948
15	Preston	146	622	41	Burton upon Trent	129	375
16	Bermondsey	144	367	42	Halifax	129	671
17	Hamilton Burgh	143	358	43	Fulham	128	568
18	Rutherglen Burgh	141	181	44	Paddington	128	615
19	Poplar	141	469	45	Rochdale	127	733
20	Warrington	141	488	46	Hackney	127	898
21	Bootle	141	507	47	Motherwell & Wishaw Burgh	127	529
22	Gateshead	140	661	48	Kilmarnock Burgh	127	383
23	Holborn	140	120	49	Islington	127	1,116
24	Newcastle upon Tyne	139	1,505	50	Dumfries Burgh	126	230
25	Stepney	138	619	51	Barrow-in-Furness	126	495
26	Airdrie Burgh	137	365	52	Stoke-on-Trent	126	1,849

Table 16: **Relationship between health inequalities and poverty**

Health decile	SMR	Poverty indicators		
		residents in households with no car	children in households with no work	adults under 65 with a long term illness
Worst	142	40.8%	33.2%	9.7%
2	121	31.4%	24.2%	8.4%
3	111	30.8%	21.0%	8.0%
4	105	26.2%	19.9%	8.3%
5	99	23.1%	15.2%	6.9%
6	94	22.3%	15.7%	6.4%
7	91	19.7%	14.1%	6.0%
8	86	17.0%	11.6%	5.6%
9	80	13.0%	9.6%	4.9%
Best	76	10.9%	7.9%	4.5%
Britain		23.6%	17.4%	6.9%

Appendix 1

Standardised mortality ratios by place, and the constitution of the 1950s areas used in this report

The contemporary standardised mortality rate for each period is given, followed by the geographical constitution of each place in terms of 1991 district population (with standardised mortality ratios for all six age groups for the 1990-92 districts shown in brackets for comparison with the latest period).

London

City of London 1950-53: **89** 1959-63: **74** 1969-73: **100** 1981-85: **87** 1986-89: **71** 1990-92: **88** is comprised of 100% of City of London (88)

Battersea 1950-53: **101** 1959-63: **100** 1969-73: **113** 1981-85: **117** 1986-89: **116** 1990-92: **121** is comprised of 32% of Wandsworth (113)

Bermondsey 1950-53: **104** 1959-63: **101** 1969-73: **109** 1981-85: **106** 1986-89: **109** 1990-92: **114** is comprised of 20% of Southwark (109)

Bethnal Green 1950-53: **104** 1959-63: **100** 1969-73: **85** 1981-85: **119** 1986-89: **124** 1990-92: **111** is comprised of 16% of Tower Hamlets (109)

Camberwell 1950-53: **104** 1959-63: **101** 1969-73: **107** 1981-85: **107** 1986-89: **107** 1990-92: **106** is comprised of 58% of Southwark (109)

Chelsea 1950-53: **102** 1959-63: **115** 1969-73: **84** 1981-85: **103** 1986-89: **95** 1990-92: **92** is comprised of 24% of Kensington and Chelsea (97)

Deptford 1950-53: **106** 1959-63: **97** 1969-73: **109** 1981-85: **111** 1986-89: **108** 1990-92: **112** is comprised of 22% of Lewisham (107)

Finsbury 1950-53: **106** 1959-63: **99** 1969-73: **86** 1981-85: **102** 1986-89: **102** 1990-92: **107** is comprised of 10% of Islington (108)

Fulham 1950-53: **99** 1959-63: **93** 1969-73: **102** 1981-85: **103** 1986-89: **105** 1990-92: **103** is comprised of 51% of Hammersmith and Fulham (109)

Greenwich 1950-53: **97** 1959-63: **93** 1969-73: **97** 1981-85: **104** 1986-89: **103** 1990-92: **106** is comprised of 34% of Greenwich (103)

Hackney 1950-53: **99** 1959-63: **99** 1969-73: **109** 1981-85: **109** 1986-89: **110** 1990-92: **116** is comprised of 70% of Hackney (114)

Hammersmith 1950-53: **101** 1959-63: **97** 1969-73: **104** 1981-85: **111** 1986-89: **109** 1990-92: **116** is comprised of 49% of Hammersmith and Fulham (109)

Hampstead 1950-53: **93** 1959-63: **89** 1969-73: **106** 1981-85: **92** 1986-89: **97** 1990-92: **98** is comprised of 44% of Camden (104)

Holborn 1950-53: **99** 1959-63: **96** 1969-73: **67** 1981-85: **102** 1986-89: **117** 1990-92: **98** is comprised of 7% of Camden (104)

Islington 1950-53: **104** 1959-63: **102** 1969-73: **111** 1981-85: **105** 1986-89: **106** 1990-92: **108** is comprised of 90% of Islington (108)

Kensington 1950-53: **96** 1959-63: **95** 1969-73: **112** 1981-85: **104** 1986-89: **101** 1990-92: **100** is comprised of 76% of Kensington and Chelsea (97)

Lambeth 1950-53: **102** 1959-63: **99** 1969-73: **103** 1981-85: **110** 1986-89: **112** 1990-92: **113** is comprised of 68% of Lambeth (109)

Lewisham 1950-53: **96** 1959-63: **95** 1969-73: **99** 1981-85: **100** 1986-89: **104** 1990-92: **106** is comprised of 78% of Lewisham (107)

Paddington 1950-53: **104** 1959-63: **95** 1969-73: **117** 1981-85: **106** 1986-89: **106** 1990-92: **104** is comprised of 44% of City of Westminster (95)

Poplar 1950-53: **107** 1959-63: **102** 1969-73: **119** 1981-85: **117** 1986-89: **117** 1990-92: **107** is comprised of 35% of Tower Hamlets (109)

St Marylebone 1950-53: **102** 1959-63: **110** 1969-73: **85** 1981-85: **90** 1986-89: **92** 1990-92: **86** is comprised of 27% of City of Westminster (95)

St Pancras 1950-53: **100** 1959-63: **96** 1969-73: **100** 1981-85: **112** 1986-89: **109** 1990-92: **111** is comprised of 49% of Camden (104)

Shoreditch 1950-53: **115** 1959-63: **119** 1969-73: **81** 1981-85: **119** 1986-89: **102** 1990-92: **115** is comprised of 10% of Hackney (114)

Southwark 1950-53: **116** 1959-63: **124** 1969-73: **106** 1981-85: **103** 1986-89: **110** 1990-92: **114** is comprised of 22% of Southwark (109)

Stepney 1950-53: **118** 1959-63: **116** 1969-73: **111** 1981-85: **113** 1986-89: **111** 1990-92: **111** is comprised of 48% of Tower Hamlets (109)

Stoke Newington 1950-53: **103** 1959-63: **105** 1969-73: **108** 1981-85: **108** 1986-89: **116** 1990-92: **108** is comprised of 20% of Hackney (114)

Wandsworth 1950-53: **100** 1959-63: **114** 1969-73: **106** 1981-85: **107** 1986-89: **106** 1990-92: **108** is comprised of 32% of Lambeth (109) & 68% of Wandsworth (113)

Westminster 1950-53: **90** 1959-63: **88** 1969-73: **80** 1981-85: **100** 1986-89: **96** 1990-92: **94** is comprised of 29% of City of Westminster (95)

Woolwich 1950-53: **99** 1959-63: **91** 1969-73: **102** 1981-85: **103** 1986-89: **103** 1990-92: **102** is comprised of 66% of Greenwich (103)

County boroughs

Barnsley 1950-53: **110** 1959-63: **107** 1969-73: **108** 1981-85: **106** 1986-89: **112** 1990-92: **111** is comprised of 31% of Barnsley (107)

Barrow-in-Furness 1950-53: **108** 1959-63: **104** 1969-73: **110** 1981-85: **111** 1986-89: **112** 1990-92: **110** is comprised of 84% of Barrow-in-Furness (107)

Bath 1950-53: **95** 1959-63: **98** 1969-73: **94** 1981-85: **96** 1986-89: **96** 1990-92: **92** is comprised of 94% of Bath (90)

Birkenhead 1950-53: **112** 1959-63: **109** 1969-73: **113** 1981-85: **112** 1986-89: **116** 1990-92: **121** is comprised of 35% of Wirral (110)

Birmingham 1950-53: **104** 1959-63: **106** 1969-73: **106** 1981-85: **108** 1986-89: **108** 1990-92: **107** is comprised of 91% of Birmingham (105)

Blackburn 1950-53: **113** 1959-63: **121** 1969-73: **123** 1981-85: **122** 1986-89: **124** 1990-92: **122** is comprised of 69% of Blackburn (118)

Blackpool 1950-53: **106** 1959-63: **101** 1969-73: **102** 1981-85: **111** 1986-89: **109** 1990-92: **112** is comprised of 100% of Blackpool (112)

Bolton 1950-53: **117** 1959-63: **109** 1969-73: **120** 1981-85: **112** 1986-89: **113** 1990-92: **118** is comprised of 50% of Bolton (110)

Bootle 1950-53: **112** 1959-63: **116** 1969-73: **116** 1981-85: **108** 1986-89: **110** 1990-92: **110** is comprised of 20% of Sefton (105)

Bournemouth 1950-53: **89** 1959-63: **85** 1969-73: **91** 1981-85: **99** 1986-89: **99** 1990-92: **101** is comprised of 100% of Bournemouth (101)

Bradford 1950-53: **115** 1959-63: **114** 1969-73: **120** 1981-85: **116** 1986-89: **117** 1990-92: **116** is comprised of 58% of Bradford (110)

Brighton 1950-53: **99** 1959-63: **99** 1969-73: **100** 1981-85: **102** 1986-89: **100** 1990-92: **98** is comprised of 100% of Brighton (98)

Bristol 1950-53: **98** 1959-63: **101** 1969-73: **100** 1981-85: **101** 1986-89: **101** 1990-92: **100** is comprised of 100% of Bristol (100)

Burnley 1950-53: **118** 1959-63: **124** 1969-73: **119** 1981-85: **124** 1986-89: **119** 1990-92: **121** is comprised of 74% of Burnley (120)

Burton upon Trent 1950-53: **105** 1959-63: **110** 1969-73: **107** 1981-85: **117** 1986-89: **113** 1990-92: **112** is comprised of 49% of East Staffordshire (104)

Bury 1950-53: **111** 1959-63: **119** 1969-73: **116** 1981-85: **106** 1986-89: **102** 1990-92: **109** is comprised of 37% of Bury (110)

Canterbury 1950-53: **93** 1959-63: **99** 1969-73: **96** 1981-85: **107** 1986-89: **104** 1990-92: **93** is comprised of 29% of Canterbury (99)

Carlisle 1950-53: **115** 1959-63: **113** 1969-73: **109** 1981-85: **104** 1986-89: **104** 1990-92: **107** is comprised of 68% of Carlisle (106)

Chester 1950-53: **102** 1959-63: **100** 1969-73: **112** 1981-85: **100** 1986-89: **103** 1990-92: **101** is comprised of 35% of Chester (100)

Coventry 1950-53: **97** 1959-63: **94** 1969-73: **95** 1981-85: **100** 1986-89: **104** 1990-92: **101** is comprised of 100% of Coventry (101)

Croydon 1950-53: **93** 1959-63: **99** 1969-73: **99** 1981-85: **99** 1986-89: **99** 1990-92: **100** is comprised of 73% of Croydon (99)

Darlington 1950-53: **103** 1959-63: **102** 1969-73: **110** 1981-85: **108** 1986-89: **109** 1990-92: **108** is comprised of 87% of Darlington (115)

Derby 1950-53: **104** 1959-63: **108** 1969-73: **78** 1981-85: **117** 1986-89: **118** 1990-92: **116** is comprised of 51% of Derby (103)

Dewsbury 1950-53: **115** 1959-63: **124** 1969-73: **122** 1981-85: **120** 1986-89: **110** 1990-92: **119** is comprised of 13% of Kirklees (106)

Doncaster 1950-53: **103** 1959-63: **100** 1969-73: **104** 1981-85: **107** 1986-89: **111** 1990-92: **104** is comprised of 25% of Doncaster (101)

Dudley 1950-53: **106** 1959-63: **102** 1969-73: **76** 1981-85: **111** 1986-89: **115** 1990-92: **109** is comprised of 16% of Dudley (98)

Eastbourne 1950-53: **90** 1959-63: **91** 1969-73: **90** 1981-85: **100** 1986-89: **101** 1990-92: **103** is comprised of 100% of Eastbourne (103)

East Ham 1950-53: **95** 1959-63: **92** 1969-73: **107** 1981-85: **97** 1986-89: **97** 1990-92: **101** is comprised of 46% of Newham (108)

Exeter 1950-53: **101** 1959-63: **99** 1969-73: **100** 1981-85: **101** 1986-89: **100** 1990-92: **104** is comprised of 90% of Exeter (101)

Gateshead 1950-53: **117** 1959-63: **111** 1969-73: **111** 1981-85: **116** 1986-89: **123** 1990-92: **118** is comprised of 36% of Gateshead (111)

Gloucester 1950-53: **99** 1959-63: **101** 1969-73: **88** 1981-85: **107** 1986-89: **107** 1990-92: **98** is comprised of 65% of Gloucester (94)

Great Yarmouth 1950-53: **102** 1959-63: **98** 1969-73: **104** 1981-85: **107** 1986-89: **110** 1990-92: **111** is comprised of 54% of Great Yarmouth (101)

Grimsby 1950-53: **100** 1959-63: **97** 1969-73: **109** 1981-85: **104** 1986-89: **104** 1990-92: **109** is comprised of 100% of Great Grimsby (109)

Halifax 1950-53: **114** 1959-63: **119** 1969-73: **130** 1981-85: **121** 1986-89: **123** 1990-92: **118** is comprised of 45% of Calderdale (109)

Hastings 1950-53: **96** 1959-63: **100** 1969-73: **105** 1981-85: **117** 1986-89: **112** 1990-92: **115** is comprised of 100% of Hastings (115)

Huddersfield 1950-53: **109** 1959-63: **109** 1969-73: **110** 1981-85: **110** 1986-89: **112** 1990-92: **114** is comprised of 32% of Kirklees (106)

Ipswich 1950-53: **91** 1959-63: **91** 1969-73: **90** 1981-85: **90** 1986-89: **92** 1990-92: **94** is comprised of 100% of Ipswich (94)

Kingston upon Hull 1950-53: **110** 1959-63: **106** 1969-73: **104** 1981-85: **107** 1986-89: **107** 1990-92: **105** is comprised of 100% of Kingston upon Hull (105)

Leeds 1950-53: **112** 1959-63: **106** 1969-73: **103** 1981-85: **108** 1986-89: **107** 1990-92: **104** is comprised of 63% of Leeds (101)

Leicester 1950-53: **100** 1959-63: **103** 1969-73: **102** 1981-85: **104** 1986-89: **107** 1990-92: **107** is comprised of 100% of Leicester (107)

Lincoln 1950-53: **97** 1959-63: **94** 1969-73: **100** 1981-85: **105** 1986-89: **101** 1990-92: **102** is comprised of 100% of Lincoln (102)

Liverpool 1950-53: **118** 1959-63: **115** 1969-73: **115** 1981-85: **115** 1986-89: **116** 1990-92: **117** is comprised of 100% of Liverpool (116)

Manchester 1950-53: **118** 1959-63: **118** 1969-73: **114** 1981-85: **117** 1986-89: **119** 1990-92: **121** is comprised of 100% of Manchester (121)

Middlesbrough 1950-53: **117** 1959-63: **118** 1969-73: **85** 1981-85: **117** 1986-89: **116** 1990-92: **122** is comprised of 77% of Middlesbrough (117)

Newcastle upon Tyne 1950-53: **112** 1959-63: **106** 1969-73: **109** 1981-85: **112** 1986-89: **115** 1990-92: **119** is comprised of 69% of Newcastle upon Tyne (114)

Northampton 1950-53: **98** 1959-63: **97** 1969-73: **86** 1981-85: **104** 1986-89: **108** 1990-92: **105** is comprised of 69% of Northampton (102)

Norwich 1950-53: **96** 1959-63: **95** 1969-73: **92** 1981-85: **93** 1986-89: **93** 1990-92: **95** is comprised of 100% of Norwich (95)

Nottingham 1950-53: **104** 1959-63: **106** 1969-73: **109** 1981-85: **109** 1986-89: **110** 1990-92: **104** is comprised of 100% of Nottingham (104)

Oldham 1950-53: **120** 1959-63: **117** 1969-73: **126** 1981-85: **121** 1986-89: **124** 1990-92: **131** is comprised of 41% of Oldham (116)

Oxford 1950-53: **91** 1959-63: **90** 1969-73: **90** 1981-85: **95** 1986-89: **96** 1990-92: **96** is comprised of 100% of Oxford (96)

Plymouth 1950-53: **105** 1959-63: **106** 1969-73: **84** 1981-85: **102** 1986-89: **103** 1990-92: **104** is comprised of 67% of Plymouth (100)

Portsmouth 1950-53: **100** 1959-63: **103** 1969-73: **103** 1981-85: **106** 1986-89: **103** 1990-92: **107** is comprised of 100% of Portsmouth (107)

Preston 1950-53: **115** 1959-63: **107** 1969-73: **102** 1981-85: **115** 1986-89: **112** 1990-92: **118** is comprised of 56% of Preston (117)

Reading 1950-53: **93** 1959-63: **96** 1969-73: **94** 1981-85: **102** 1986-89: **104** 1990-92: **100** is comprised of 96% of Reading (97)

Rochdale 1950-53: **118** 1959-63: **119** 1969-73: **109** 1981-85: **112** 1986-89: **110** 1990-92: **117** is comprised of 47% of Rochdale (115)

Rotherham 1950-53: **100** 1959-63: **106** 1969-73: **106** 1981-85: **109** 1986-89: **109** 1990-92: **106** is comprised of 32% of Rotherham (103)

St Helens 1950-53: **111** 1959-63: **110** 1969-73: **113** 1981-85: **122** 1986-89: **119** 1990-92: **109** is comprised of 53% of St Helens (106)

Salford 1950-53: **121** 1959-63: **125** 1969-73: **123** 1981-85: **125** 1986-89: **126** 1990-92: **131** is comprised of 36% of Salford (117)

Sheffield 1950-53: **105** 1959-63: **103** 1969-73: **97** 1981-85: **103** 1986-89: **107** 1990-92: **106** is comprised of 79% of Sheffield (104)

Smethwick 1950-53: **98** 1959-63: **102** 1969-73: **123** 1981-85: **103** 1986-89: **110** 1990-92: **115** is comprised of 15% of Sandwell (105)

Southampton 1950-53: **99** 1959-63: **95** 1969-73: **86** 1981-85: **98** 1986-89: **99** 1990-92: **101** is comprised of 85% of Southampton (100)

Southend-on-Sea 1950-53: **93** 1959-63: **92** 1969-73: **99** 1981-85: **101** 1986-89: **104** 1990-92: **104** is comprised of 100% of Southend-on-Sea (104)

Southport 1950-53: **104** 1959-63: **103** 1969-73: **105** 1981-85: **109** 1986-89: **115** 1990-92: **112** is comprised of 31% of Sefton (105)

South Shields 1950-53: **114** 1959-63: **109** 1969-73: **108** 1981-85: **112** 1986-89: **116** 1990-92: **109** is comprised of 53% of South Tyneside (109)

Stockport 1950-53: **115** 1959-63: **110** 1969-73: **110** 1981-85: **115** 1986-89: **120** 1990-92: **116** is comprised of 46% of Stockport (103)

Stoke-on-Trent 1950-53: **117** 1959-63: **113** 1969-73: **108** 1981-85: **114** 1986-89: **111** 1990-92: **111** is comprised of 95% of Stoke-on-Trent (110)

Sunderland 1950-53: **112** 1959-63: **102** 1969-73: **93** 1981-85: **107** 1986-89: **111** 1990-92: **117** is comprised of 34% of Sunderland (114)

Tynemouth 1950-53: **110** 1959-63: **106** 1969-73: **111** 1981-85: **108** 1986-89: **105** 1990-92: **108** is comprised of 29% of North Tyneside (109)

Wakefield 1950-53: **100** 1959-63: **114** 1969-73: **123** 1981-85: **127** 1986-89: **114** 1990-92: **111** is comprised of 19% of Wakefield (104)

Wallasey 1950-53: **105** 1959-63: **105** 1969-73: **107** 1981-85: **111** 1986-89: **109** 1990-92: **116** is comprised of 26% of Wirral (110)

Walsall 1950-53: **111** 1959-63: **106** 1969-73: **99** 1981-85: **109** 1986-89: **108** 1990-92: **108** is comprised of 40% of Walsall (104)

Warrington 1950-53: **110** 1959-63: **113** 1969-73: **112** 1981-85: **114** 1986-89: **117** 1990-92: **114** is comprised of 31% of Warrington (108)

West Bromwich 1950-53: **110** 1959-63: **109** 1969-73: **110** 1981-85: **103** 1986-89: **103** 1990-92: **103** is comprised of 33% of Sandwell (105)

West Ham 1950-53: **102** 1959-63: **102** 1969-73: **97** 1981-85: **109** 1986-89: **117** 1990-92: **115** is comprised of 54% of Newham (108)

West Hartlepool 1950-53: **112** 1959-63: **110** 1969-73: **109** 1981-85: **112** 1986-89: **113** 1990-92: **111** is comprised of 77% of Hartlepool (111)

Wigan 1950-53: **121** 1959-63: **110** 1969-73: **129** 1981-85: **113** 1986-89: **112** 1990-92: **109** is comprised of 24% of Wigan (109)

Wolverhampton 1950-53: **103** 1959-63: **103** 1969-73: **97** 1981-85: **107** 1986-89: **108** 1990-92: **106** is comprised of 58% of Wolverhampton (103)

Worcester 1950-53: **100** 1959-63: **102** 1969-73: **94** 1981-85: **102** 1986-89: **94** 1990-92: **92** is comprised of 100% of Worcester (92)

York 1950-53: **103** 1959-63: **101** 1969-73: **102** 1981-85: **105** 1986-89: **104** 1990-92: **99** is comprised of 100% of York (99)

Welsh county boroughs

Cardiff 1950-53: **108** 1959-63: **102** 1969-73: **98** 1981-85: **107** 1986-89: **104** 1990-92: **106** is comprised of 71% of Cardiff (99)

Merthyr Tydfil 1950-53: **120** 1959-63: **118** 1969-73: **112** 1981-85: **114** 1986-89: **117** 1990-92: **114** is comprised of 90% of Merthyr Tydfil (111)

Newport 1950-53: **104** 1959-63: **104** 1969-73: **105** 1981-85: **106** 1986-89: **105** 1990-92: **106** is comprised of 76% of Newport (103)

Swansea 1950-53: **108** 1959-63: **109** 1969-73: **108** 1981-85: **104** 1986-89: **101** 1990-92: **99** is comprised of 90% of Swansea (98)

County remainders

Bedfordshire UA 1950-53: **92** 1959-63: **93** 1969-73: **96** 1981-85: **95** 1986-89: **98** 1990-92: **101** is comprised of 100% of Luton (101) & 26% of Mid Bedfordshire (98) & 67% of North Bedfordshire (96) & 50% of South Bedfordshire (97)

Bedfordshire RD 1950-53: **88** 1959-63: **92** 1969-73: **94** 1981-85: **93** 1986-89: **95** 1990-92: **94** is comprised of 74% of Mid Bedfordshire (98) & 33% of North Bedfordshire (96) & 39% of South Bedfordshire (97)

Berkshire UA 1950-53: **101** 1959-63: **104** 1969-73: **98** 1981-85: **96** 1986-89: **94** 1990-92: **90** is comprised of 20% of Newbury (93) & 56% of Windsor and Maidenhead (94) & 21% of Wokingham (86) & 5% of South Oxfordshire (91) & 37% of Vale of White Horse (83)

Berkshire RD 1950-53: **87** 1959-63: **88** 1969-73: **89** 1981-85: **87** 1986-89: **90** 1990-92: **92** is comprised of 100% of Bracknell (98) & 80% of Newbury (93) & 34% of Windsor and Maidenhead (94) & 79% of Wokingham (86) & 19% of South Oxfordshire (91) & 63% of Vale of White Horse (83)

Buckinghamshire UA 1950-53: **90** 1959-63: **91** 1969-73: **87** 1981-85: **95** 1986-89: **94** 1990-92: **94** is comprised of 11% of South Bedfordshire (97) & 91% of Slough (93) & 3% of Windsor and Maidenhead (94) & 43% of Aylesbury Vale (96) & 23% of Chiltern (87) & 52% of Milton Keynes (95) & 17% of South Bucks (94) & 49% of Wycombe (90)

Buckinghamshire RD 1950-53: **86** 1959-63: **88** 1969-73: **88** 1981-85: **88** 1986-89: **90** 1990-92: **92** is comprised of 9% of Slough (93) & 7% of Windsor and Maidenhead (94) & 57% of Aylesbury Vale (96) & 77% of Chiltern (87) & 48% of Milton Keynes (95) & 83% of South Bucks (94) & 51% of Wycombe (90)

Cambridgeshire UA 1950-53: **88** 1959-63: **88** 1969-73: **89** 1981-85: **89** 1986-89: **90** 1990-92: **91** is comprised of 100% of Cambridge (91)

Cambridgeshire RD 1950-53: **89** 1959-63: **92** 1969-73: **93** 1981-85: **85** 1986-89: **86** 1990-92: **88** is comprised of 48% of East Cambridgeshire (92) & 100% of South Cambridgeshire (87)

Cheshire UA 1950-53: **100** 1959-63: **102** 1969-73: **98** 1981-85: **99** 1986-89: **99** 1990-92: **99** is comprised of 54% of Stockport (103) & 42% of Tameside (109) & 55% of Trafford (100) & 38% of Wirral (110) & 13% of Chester (100) & 75% of Congleton (98) & 61% of Crewe and Nantwich (100) & 100% of Ellesmere Port and Neston (98) & 33% of Halton (107) & 68% of Macclesfield (98) & 40% of Vale Royal (99) & 6% of Warrington (108)

Cheshire RD 1950-53: **94** 1959-63: **101** 1969-73: **112** 1981-85: **97** 1986-89: **95** 1990-92: **100** is comprised of 4% of Trafford (100) & 52% of Chester (100) & 25% of Congleton (98) & 39% of Crewe and Nantwich (100) & 20% of Halton (107) & 32% of Macclesfield (98) & 60% of Vale Royal (99) & 14% of Warrington (108) & 2% of High Peak (106)

Cornwall UA 1950-53: **101** 1959-63: **101** 1969-73: **99** 1981-85: **103** 1986-89: **100** 1990-92: **101** is comprised of 46% of Caradon (90) & 50% of Carrick (92) & 65% of Kerrier (98) & 42% of North Cornwall (96) & 60% of Penwith (95) & 70% of Restormel (97)

Cornwall RD 1950-53: **95** 1959-63: **90** 1969-73: **89** 1981-85: **86** 1986-89: **86** 1990-92: **87** is comprised of 54% of Caradon (90) & 50% of Carrick (92) & 35% of Kerrier (98) & 55% of North Cornwall (96) & 40% of Penwith (95) & 30% of Restormel (97) & 100% of Isles of Scilly (97)

Cumberland UA 1950-53: **112** 1959-63: **110** 1969-73: **109** 1981-85: **114** 1986-89: **113** 1990-92: **119** is comprised of 53% of Allerdale (108) & 36% of Copeland (113) & 29% of Eden (102)

Cumberland RD 1950-53: **103** 1959-63: **103** 1969-73: **104** 1981-85: **104** 1986-89: **101** 1990-92: **103** is comprised of 47% of Allerdale (108) & 32% of Carlisle (106) & 64% of Copeland (113) & 32% of Eden (102)

Derbyshire UA 1950-53: **99** 1959-63: **101** 1969-73: **102** 1981-85: **102** 1986-89: **102** 1990-92: **104** is comprised of 76% of Amber Valley (100) & 16% of Bolsover (103) & 90% of Chesterfield (106) & 66% of Erewash (102) & 73% of High Peak (106) & 31% of North East Derbyshire (94) & 35% of South Derbyshire (105) & 55% of West Derbyshire (97)

Derbyshire RD 1950-53: **96** 1959-63: **95** 1969-73: **117** 1981-85: **96** 1986-89: **95** 1990-92: **96** is comprised of 6% of Sheffield (104) & 24% of Amber Valley (100) & 84% of Bolsover (103) & 10% of Chesterfield (106) & 49% of Derby (103) & 34% of Erewash (102) & 25% of High Peak (106) & 69% of North East Derbyshire (94) & 65% of South Derbyshire (105) & 45% of West Derbyshire (97)

Devon UA 1950-53: **97** 1959-63: **93** 1969-73: **91** 1981-85: **97** 1986-89: **98** 1990-92: **98** is comprised of 65% of East Devon (91) & 36% of Mid Devon (95) & 43% of North Devon (93) & 26% of South Hams (88) & 52% of Teignbridge (96) & 100% of Torbay (99) & 57% of Torridge (90) & 32% of West Devon (100)

Devon RD 1950-53: **91** 1959-63: **89** 1969-73: **101** 1981-85: **87** 1986-89: **87** 1990-92: **89** is comprised of 2% of North Cornwall (96) & 35% of East Devon (91) & 10% of Exeter (101) & 64% of Mid Devon (95) & 57% of North Devon (93) & 33% of Plymouth (100) & 74% of South Hams (88) & 48% of Teignbridge (96) & 43% of Torridge (90) & 68% of West Devon (100)

Dorset UA 1950-53: **95** 1959-63: **94** 1969-73: **92** 1981-85: **94** 1986-89: **95** 1990-92: **96** is comprised of 21% of North Dorset (85) & 100% of Poole (93) & 35% of Purbeck (89) & 38% of West Dorset (90) & 100% of Weymouth and Portland (98) & 8% of Wimborne (76)

Dorset RD 1950-53: **90** 1959-63: **89** 1969-73: **85** 1981-85: **77** 1986-89: **78** 1990-92: **79** is comprised of 79% of North Dorset (85) & 65% of Purbeck (89) & 62% of West Dorset (90) & 84% of Wimborne (76)

Durham UA 1950-53: **109** 1959-63: **107** 1969-73: **110** 1981-85: **110** 1986-89: **109** 1990-92: **111** is comprised of 55% of Gateshead (111) & 47% of South Tyneside (109) & 36% of Sunderland (114) & 19% of Hartlepool (111) & 68% of Stockton-on-Tees (108) & 38% of Chester-le-Street (100) & 84% of Derwentside (118) & 51% of Durham (100) & 20% of Easington (116) & 39% of Sedgefield (108) & 20% of Teesdale (99) & 88% of Wear Valley (113)

Durham RD 1950-53: **108** 1959-63: **109** 1969-73: **117** 1981-85: **109** 1986-89: **110** 1990-92: **111** is comprised of 8% of Gateshead (111) & 29% of Sunderland (114) & 4% of Hartlepool (111) & 10% of Stockton-on-Tees (108) & 62% of Chester-le-Street (100) & 13% of Darlington (115) & 16% of Derwentside (118) & 49% of Durham (100) & 80% of Easington (116) & 61% of Sedgefield (108) & 64% of Teesdale (99) & 12% of Wear Valley (113)

Ely, Isle of UA 1950-53: **97** 1959-63: **102** 1969-73: **99** 1981-85: **106** 1986-89: **108** 1990-92: **96** is comprised of 17% of East Cambridgeshire (92) & 75% of Fenland (94)

Ely, Isle of RD 1950-53: **85** 1959-63: **86** 1969-73: **82** 1981-85: **85** 1986-89: **93** 1990-92: **91** is comprised of 35% of East Cambridgeshire (92) & 25% of Fenland (94) & 1% of Peterborough (95)

Essex UA 1950-53: **93** 1959-63: **93** 1969-73: **92** 1981-85: **96** 1986-89: **95** 1990-92: **96** is comprised of 100% of Barking and Dagenham (101) & 100% of Havering (90) & 100% of Redbridge (99) & 100% of Waltham Forest (104) & 100% of Basildon (90) & 57% of Braintree (95) & 77% of Brentwood (105) & 100% of Castle Point (86) & 40% of Chelmsford (83) & 70% of Colchester (94) & 71% of Epping Forest (87) & 46% of Maldon (98) & 39% of Rochford (92) & 71% of Tendring (98) & 100% of Thurrock (99) & 21% of Uttlesford (93)

Essex RD 1950-53: **89** 1959-63: **93** 1969-73: **97** 1981-85: **88** 1986-89: **89** 1990-92: **90** is comprised of 43% of Braintree (95) & 23% of Brentwood (105) & 60% of Chelmsford (83) & 30% of Colchester (94) & 29% of Epping Forest (87) & 100% of Harlow (91) & 54% of Maldon (98) & 61% of Rochford (92) & 29% of Tendring (98) & 79% of Uttlesford (93)

Gloucestershire UA 1950-53: **100** 1959-63: **98** 1969-73: **97** 1981-85: **97** 1986-89: **98** 1990-92: **97** is comprised of 60% of Kingswood (91) & 100% of Cheltenham (102) & 23% of Cotswold (86) & 25% of Stroud (90) & 11% of Tewkesbury (84)

Gloucestershire RD 1950-53: **95** 1959-63: **95** 1969-73: **96** 1981-85: **87** 1986-89: **86** 1990-92: **88** is comprised of 40% of Kingswood (91) & 100% of Northavon (87) & 77% of Cotswold (86) & 100% of Forest of Dean (95) & 35% of Gloucester (94) & 75% of Stroud (90) & 89% of Tewkesbury (84)

Hampshire UA 1950-53: **92** 1959-63: **91** 1969-73: **89** 1981-85: **90** 1986-89: **91** 1990-92: **91** is comprised of 90% of Christchurch (85) & 48% of Basingstoke and Deane (89) & 28% of East Hampshire (94) & 51% of Eastleigh (88) & 100% of Fareham (89) & 100% of Gosport (94) & 31% of Hart (83) & 81% of Havant (88) & 27% of New Forest (88) & 100% of Rushmoor (96) & 49% of Test Valley (93) & 31% of Winchester (96)

Hampshire RD 1950-53: **91** 1959-63: **96** 1969-73: **98** 1981-85: **91** 1986-89: **89** 1990-92: **89** is comprised of 10% of Christchurch (85) & 8% of Wimborne (76) & 52% of Basingstoke and Deane (89) & 72% of East Hampshire (94) & 49% of Eastleigh (88) & 69% of Hart (83) & 19% of Havant (88) & 73% of New Forest (88) & 15% of Southampton (100) & 51% of Test Valley (93) & 69% of Winchester (96)

Herefordshire UA 1950-53: **101** 1959-63: **101** 1969-73: **95** 1981-85: **99** 1986-89: **99** 1990-92: **97** is comprised of 100% of Hereford (96) & 31% of Leominster (99) & 10% of Malvern Hills (97) & 19% of South Herefordshire (99)

Herefordshire RD 1950-53: **90** 1959-63: **92** 1969-73: **93** 1981-85: **87** 1986-89: **87** 1990-92: **95** is comprised of 54% of Leominster (99) & 18% of Malvern Hills (97) & 81% of South Herefordshire (99)

Hertfordshire UA 1950-53: **91** 1959-63: **90** 1969-73: **94** 1981-85: **90** 1986-89: **92** 1990-92: **92** is comprised of 31% of Barnet (95) & 100% of Broxbourne (86) & 77% of Dacorum (85) & 65% of East Hertfordshire (92) & 27% of Hertsmere (101) & 76% of North Hertfordshire (99) & 62% of St Albans (93) & 100% of Stevenage (84) & 50% of Three Rivers (91) & 100% of Watford (96) & 45% of Welwyn Hatfield (86)

Hertfordshire RD 1950-53: **90** 1959-63: **102** 1969-73: **99** 1981-85: **95** 1986-89: **94** 1990-92: **91** is comprised of 23% of Dacorum (85) & 35% of East Hertfordshire (92) & 48% of Hertsmere (101) & 24% of North Hertfordshire (99) & 38% of St Albans (93) & 50% of Three Rivers (91) & 55% of Welwyn Hatfield (86)

Huntingdonshire UA 1950-53: **99** 1959-63: **102** 1969-73: **97** 1981-85: **97** 1986-89: **96** 1990-92: **95** is comprised of 47% of Huntingdon (90) & 11% of Peterborough (95)

Huntingdonshire RD 1950-53: **92** 1959-63: **89** 1969-73: **100** 1981-85: **84** 1986-89: **87** 1990-92: **86** is comprised of 53% of Huntingdon (90) & 13% of Peterborough (95)

Kent UA 1950-53: **93** 1959-63: **94** 1969-73: **95** 1981-85: **97** 1986-89: **98** 1990-92: **97** is comprised of 100% of Bexley (91) & 100% of Bromley (89) & 55% of Ashford (90) & 50% of Canterbury (99) & 65% of Dartford (108) & 62% of Dover (99) & 100% of Gillingham (93) & 82% of Gravesham (94) & 52% of Maidstone (93) & 80% of Rochester upon Medway (101) & 16% of Sevenoaks (92) & 77% of Shepway (99) & 64% of Swale (100) & 96% of Thanet (105) & 30% of Tonbridge and Malling (93) & 56% of Tunbridge Wells (104)

Kent RD 1950-53: **90** 1959-63: **96** 1969-73: **98** 1981-85: **93** 1986-89: **93** 1990-92: **94** is comprised of 45% of Ashford (90) & 21% of Canterbury (99) & 35% of Dartford (108) & 38% of Dover (99) & 18% of Gravesham (94) & 48% of Maidstone (93) & 20% of Rochester upon Medway (101) & 84% of Sevenoaks (92) & 23% of Shepway (99) & 36% of Swale (100) & 4% of Thanet (105) & 70% of Tonbridge and Malling (93) & 44% of Tunbridge Wells (104)

Lancashire UA 1950-53: **109** 1959-63: **110** 1969-73: **107** 1981-85: **108** 1986-89: **108** 1990-92: **107** is comprised of 50% of Bolton (110) & 63% of Bury (110) & 48% of Oldham (116) & 53% of Rochdale (115) & 64% of Salford (117) & 48% of Tameside (109) & 40% of Trafford (100) & 71% of Wigan (109) & 42% of Knowsley (109) & 29% of St Helens (106) & 34% of Sefton (105) & 45% of Halton (107) & 4% of Warrington (108) & 16% of Barrow-in-Furness (107) & 16% of South Lakeland (95) & 26% of Blackburn (118) & 10% of Burnley (120) & 45% of Chorley (101) & 67% of Fylde (109) & 100% of Hyndburn (110) & 77% of Lancaster (110) & 76% of Pendle (99) & 21% of Preston (117) & 41% of Ribble Valley (101) & 100% of Rossendale (117) & 58% of South Ribble (96) & 66% of West Lancashire (99) & 78% of Wyre (103)

Lancashire RD 1950-53: **97** 1959-63: **107** 1969-73: **110** 1981-85: **104** 1986-89: **103** 1990-92: **103** is comprised of 11% of Tameside (109) & 5% of Wigan (109) & 58% of Knowsley (109) & 17% of St Helens (106) & 15% of Sefton (105) & 2% of Halton (107) & 46% of Warrington (108) & 18% of South Lakeland (95) & 5% of Blackburn (118) & 16% of Burnley (120) & 55% of Chorley (101) & 33% of Fylde (109) & 23% of Lancaster (110) & 6% of Pendle (99) & 23% of Preston (117) & 48% of Ribble Valley (101) & 42% of South Ribble (96) & 34% of West Lancashire (99) & 22% of Wyre (103)

Leicestershire UA 1950-53: **94** 1959-63: **92** 1969-73: **94** 1981-85: **92** 1986-89: **93** 1990-92: **90** is comprised of 43% of Charnwood (90) & 24% of Harborough (87) & 63% of Hinckley and Bosworth (89) & 54% of Melton (93) & 57% of North West Leicestershire (94) & 100% of Oadby and Wigston (80)

Leicestershire RD 1950-53: **86** 1959-63: **93** 1969-73: **92** 1981-85: **89** 1986-89: **89** 1990-92: **89** is comprised of 100% of Blaby (87) & 57% of Charnwood (90) & 76% of Harborough (87) & 37% of Hinckley and Bosworth (89) & 46% of Melton (93) & 43% of North West Leicestershire (94)

Lincolnshire, Holland UA 1950-53: **102** 1959-63: **101** 1969-73: **98** 1981-85: **98** 1986-89: **98** 1990-92: **101** is comprised of 50% of Boston (94) & 29% of South Holland (92)

Lincolnshire, Holland RD 1950-53: **91** 1959-63: **87** 1969-73: **91** 1981-85: **89** 1986-89: **86** 1990-92: **88** is comprised of 50% of Boston (94) & 71% of South Holland (92)

Lincolnshire, Kesteven UA 1950-53: **99** 1959-63: **107** 1969-73: **108** 1981-85: **107** 1986-89: **100** 1990-92: **97** is comprised of 13% of North Kesteven (93) & 55% of South Kesteven (91)

Lincolnshire, Kesteven RD 1950-53: **91** 1959-63: **97** 1969-73: **96** 1981-85: **94** 1986-89: **89** 1990-92: **90** is comprised of 87% of North Kesteven (93) & 45% of South Kesteven (91)

Lincolnshire, Lindsey UA 1950-53: **98** 1959-63: **97** 1969-73: **102** 1981-85: **104** 1986-89: **102** 1990-92: **102** is comprised of 50% of Cleethorpes (91) & 21% of Glanford (103) & 100% of Scunthorpe (102) & 44% of East Lindsey (96) & 29% of West Lindsey (100)

Lincolnshire, Lindsey RD 1950-53: **91** 1959-63: **91** 1969-73: **94** 1981-85: **92** 1986-89: **92** 1990-92: **94** is comprised of 30% of Boothferry (101) & 50% of Cleethorpes (91) & 79% of Glanford (103) & 56% of East Lindsey (96) & 71% of West Lindsey (100)

Middlesex 1950-53: **90** 1959-63: **92** 1969-73: **94** 1981-85: **95** 1986-89: **96** 1990-92: **97** is comprised of 100% of Haringey (105) & 69% of Barnet (95) & 100% of Brent (95) & 100% of Ealing (102) & 100% of Enfield (95) & 100% of Harrow (90) & 100% of Hillingdon (94) & 100% of Hounslow (98) & 59% of Richmond upon Thames (94) & 25% of Hertsmere (101) & 100% of Spelthorne (87)

Norfolk UA 1950-53: **95** 1959-63: **97** 1969-73: **94** 1981-85: **99** 1986-89: **99** 1990-92: **98** is comprised of 36% of Breckland (91) & 28% of North Norfolk (95) & 17% of South Norfolk (89) & 34% of West Norfolk (90)

Norfolk RD 1950-53: **88** 1959-63: **92** 1969-73: **90** 1981-85: **87** 1986-89: **87** 1990-92: **89** is comprised of 64% of Breckland (91) & 100% of Broadland (91) & 27% of Great Yarmouth (101) & 72% of North Norfolk (95) & 83% of South Norfolk (89) & 66% of West Norfolk (90)

Northamptonshire UA 1950-53: **99** 1959-63: **96** 1969-73: **94** 1981-85: **97** 1986-89: **101** 1990-92: **101** is comprised of 90% of Corby (102) & 29% of Daventry (95) & 70% of East Northamptonshire (97) & 89% of Kettering (101) & 13% of South Northamptonshire (96) & 70% of Wellingborough (95)

Northamptonshire RD 1950-53: **88** 1959-63: **91** 1969-73: **104** 1981-85: **88** 1986-89: **90** 1990-92: **94** is comprised of 10% of Corby (102) & 71% of Daventry (95) & 30% of East Northamptonshire (97) & 11% of Kettering (101) & 31% of Northampton (102) & 87% of South Northamptonshire (96) & 30% of Wellingborough (95)

Northumberland UA 1950-53: **105** 1959-63: **105** 1969-73: **107** 1981-85: **109** 1986-89: **109** 1990-92: **109** is comprised of 25% of Newcastle upon Tyne (114) & 71% of North Tyneside (109) & 44% of Alnwick (101) & 46% of Berwick-upon-Tweed (97) & 100% of Blyth Valley (108) & 29% of Castle Morpeth (115) & 39% of Tynedale (107) & 100% of Wansbeck (101)

Northumberland RD 1950-53: **98** 1959-63: **109** 1969-73: **109** 1981-85: **106** 1986-89: **105** 1990-92: **102** is comprised of 6% of Newcastle upon Tyne (114) & 56% of Alnwick (101) & 54% of Berwick-upon-Tweed (97) & 71% of Castle Morpeth (115) & 61% of Tynedale (107)

Nottinghamshire UA 1950-53: **97** 1959-63: **97** 1969-73: **98** 1981-85: **98** 1986-89: **97** 1990-92: **97** is comprised of 89% of Ashfield (98) & 57% of Bassetlaw (102) & 72% of Broxtowe (93) & 79% of Gedling (97) & 100% of Mansfield (95) & 23% of Newark (100) & 34% of Rushcliffe (97)

Nottinghamshire RD 1950-53: **93** 1959-63: **94** 1969-73: **95** 1981-85: **94** 1986-89: **94** 1990-92: **98** is comprised of 11% of Ashfield (98) & 43% of Bassetlaw (102) & 28% of Broxtowe (93) & 21% of Gedling (97) & 77% of Newark (100) & 66% of Rushcliffe (97)

Oxfordshire UA 1950-53: **97** 1959-63: **102** 1969-73: **90** 1981-85: **94** 1986-89: **94** 1990-92: **92** is comprised of 49% of Cherwell (89) & 16% of South Oxfordshire (91) & 30% of West Oxfordshire (87)

Oxfordshire RD 1950-53: **87** 1959-63: **91** 1969-73: **87** 1981-85: **84** 1986-89: **87** 1990-92: **86** is comprised of 4% of Reading (97) & 51% of Cherwell (89) & 59% of South Oxfordshire (91) & 70% of West Oxfordshire (87)

Peterborough, Soke of UA 1950-53: **98** 1959-63: **95** 1969-73: **94** 1981-85: **100** 1986-89: **102** 1990-92: **100** is comprised of 63% of Peterborough (95)

Peterborough, Soke of RD 1950-53: **86** 1959-63: **83** 1969-73: **53** 1981-85: **89** 1986-89: **90** 1990-92: **86** is comprised of 11% of Peterborough (95)

Rutland UA 1950-53: **105** 1959-63: **116** 1969-73: **100** 1981-85: **103** 1986-89: **103** 1990-92: **78** is comprised of 28% of Rutland (88)

Rutland RD 1950-53: **92** 1959-63: **90** 1969-73: **93** 1981-85: **92** 1986-89: **92** 1990-92: **93** is comprised of 72% of Rutland (88)

Shropshire UA 1950-53: **104** 1959-63: **104** 1969-73: **100** 1981-85: **106** 1986-89: **102** 1990-92: **96** is comprised of 39% of Bridgnorth (96) & 48% of North Shropshire (95) & 42% of Oswestry (98) & 69% of Shrewsbury and Atcham (89) & 33% of South Shropshire (94) & 73% of The Wrekin (97)

Shropshire RD 1950-53: **94** 1959-63: **94** 1969-73: **100** 1981-85: **91** 1986-89: **90** 1990-92: **93** is comprised of 61% of Bridgnorth (96) & 52% of North Shropshire (95) & 58% of Oswestry (98) & 31% of Shrewsbury and Atcham (89) & 67% of South Shropshire (94) & 27% of The Wrekin (97)

Somerset UA 1950-53: **98** 1959-63: **95** 1969-73: **97** 1981-85: **98** 1986-89: **99** 1990-92: **97** is comprised of 51% of Wansdyke (90) & 55% of Woodspring (94) & 52% of Mendip (95) & 50% of Sedgemoor (91) & 50% of Taunton Deane (96) & 42% of West Somerset (88) & 35% of Yeovil (90)

Somerset RD 1950-53: **92** 1959-63: **91** 1969-73: **92** 1981-85: **87** 1986-89: **88** 1990-92: **88** is comprised of 6% of Bath (90) & 49% of Wansdyke (90) & 45% of Woodspring (94) & 48% of Mendip (95) & 50% of Sedgemoor (91) & 50% of Taunton Deane (96) & 58% of West Somerset (88) & 65% of Yeovil (90)

Staffordshire UA 1950-53: **106** 1959-63: **105** 1969-73: **108** 1981-85: **100** 1986-89: **100** 1990-92: **101** is comprised of 52% of Dudley (98) & 35% of Sandwell (105) & 60% of Walsall (104) & 42% of Wolverhampton (103) & 99% of Cannock Chase (94) & 11% of East Staffordshire (104) & 31% of Lichfield (107) & 81% of Newcastle-under-Lyme (100) & 56% of Stafford (105) & 41% of Staffordshire Moorlands (99) & 33% of Tamworth (89)

Staffordshire RD 1950-53: **91** 1959-63: **96** 1969-73: **98** 1981-85: **94** 1986-89: **99** 1990-92: **105** is comprised of 1% of Cannock Chase (94) & 41% of East Staffordshire (104) & 69% of Lichfield (107) & 19% of Newcastle-under-Lyme (100) & 100% of South Staffordshire (100) & 44% of Stafford (105) & 59% of Staffordshire Moorlands (99) & 5% of Stoke-on-Trent (110)

Suffolk, East UA 1950-53: **93** 1959-63: **92** 1969-73: **94** 1981-85: **94** 1986-89: **94** 1990-92: **93** is comprised of 19% of Mid Suffolk (95) & 38% of Suffolk Coastal (90) & 72% of Waveney (90)

Suffolk, East RD 1950-53: **88** 1959-63: **91** 1969-73: **91** 1981-85: **89** 1986-89: **85** 1990-92: **90** is comprised of 19% of Great Yarmouth (101) & 31% of Babergh (93) & 60% of Mid Suffolk (95) & 62% of Suffolk Coastal (90) & 28% of Waveney (90)

Suffolk, West UA 1950-53: **96** 1959-63 **102** 1969-73: **102** 1981-85: **102** 1986-89: **102** 1990-92: **100** is comprised of 22% of Babergh (93) & 31% of Forest Heath (92) & 54% of St Edmundsbury (94)

Suffolk, West RD 1950-53: **94** 1959-63: **86** 1969-73: **84** 1981-85: **87** 1986-89: **88** 1990-92: **89** is comprised of 47% of Babergh (93) & 69% of Forest Heath (92) & 21% of Mid Suffolk (95) & 46% of St Edmundsbury (94)

Surrey UA 1950-53: **90** 1959-63: **94** 1969-73: **93** 1981-85: **93** 1986-89: **94** 1990-92: **94** is comprised of 27% of Croydon (99) & 100% of Kingston upon Thames (93) & 100% of Merton (95) & 41% of Richmond upon Thames (94) & 100% of Sutton (94) & 100% of Elmbridge (85) & 100% of Epsom and Ewell (103) & 49% of Guildford (84) & 83% of Mole Valley (87) & 81% of Reigate and Banstead (99) & 100% of Runnymede (92) & 66% of Surrey Heath (93) & 43% of Tandridge (94) & 63% of Waverley (88) & 100% of Woking (93)

Surrey RD 1950-53: **86** 1959-63: **86** 1969-73: **88** 1981-85: **85** 1986-89: **88** 1990-92: **89** is comprised of 51% of Guildford (84) & 17% of Mole Valley (87) & 19% of Reigate and Banstead (99) & 34% of Surrey Heath (93) & 57% of Tandridge (94) & 37% of Waverley (88)

Sussex, East UA 1950-53: **91** 1959-63: **91** 1969-73: **92** 1981-85: **97** 1986-89: **103** 1990-92: **104** is comprised of 100% of Hove (114) & 53% of Lewes (94) & 53% of Rother (96) & 62% of Mid Sussex (90)

Sussex, East RD 1950-53: **86** 1959-63: **89** 1969-73: **92** 1981-85: **88** 1986-89: **85** 1990-92: **87** is comprised of 47% of Lewes (94) & 47% of Rother (96) & 100% of Wealden (88) & 28% of Crawley (88) & 38% of Mid Sussex (90)

Sussex, West UA 1950-53: **90** 1959-63: **90** 1969-73: **83** 1981-85: **105** 1986-89: **104** 1990-92: **106** is comprised of 55% of Adur (89) & 52% of Arun (98) & 23% of Chichester (94) & 28% of Horsham (92) & 100% of Worthing (112)

Sussex, West RD 1950-53: **87** 1959-63: **88** 1969-73: **98** 1981-85: **88** 1986-89: **90** 1990-92: **90** is comprised of 45% of Adur (89) & 48% of Arun (98) & 77% of Chichester (94) & 72% of Crawley (88) & 72% of Horsham (92)

Warwickshire UA 1950-53: **94** 1959-63: **95** 1969-73: **93** 1981-85: **94** 1986-89: **94** 1990-92: **92** is comprised of 9% of Birmingham (105) & 60% of Solihull (85) & 100% of Nuneaton and Bedworth (100) & 69% of Rugby (95) & 21% of Stratford-on-Avon (92) & 75% of Warwick (95)

Warwickshire RD 1950-53: **92** 1959-63: **94** 1969-73: **108** 1981-85: **94** 1986-89: **91** 1990-92: **94** is comprised of 40% of Solihull (85) & 67% of Tamworth (89) & 100% of North Warwickshire (99) & 31% of Rugby (95) & 79% of Stratford-on-Avon (92) & 25% of Warwick (95)

Westmorland UA 1950-53: **98** 1959-63: **99** 1969-73: **90** 1981-85: **95** 1986-89: **98** 1990-92: 98 is comprised of 6% of Eden (102) & 39% of South Lakeland (95)

Westmorland RD 1950-53: **94** 1959-63: **91** 1969-73: **88** 1981-85: **90** 1986-89: **97** 1990-92: **89** is comprised of 33% of Eden (102) & 23% of South Lakeland (95)

Wight, Isle of UA 1950-53: **96** 1959-63: **97** 1969-73: **93** 1981-85: **96** 1986-89: **101** 1990-92: **101** is comprised of 100% of Medina (97) & 47% of South Wight (98)

Wight, Isle of RD 1950-53: **89** 1959-63: **82** 1969-73: **90** 1981-85: **88** 1986-89: **87** 1990-92: **91** is comprised of 53% of South Wight (98)

Wiltshire UA 1950-53: **97** 1959-63: **97** 1969-73: **93** 1981-85: **96** 1986-89: **98** 1990-92: **96** is comprised of 26% of Kennet (93) & 26% of North Wiltshire (93) & 39% of Salisbury (94) & 61% of Thamesdown (97) & 65% of West Wiltshire (94)

Wiltshire RD 1950-53: **87** 1959-63: **93** 1969-73: **97** 1981-85: **92** 1986-89: **92** 1990-92: **93** is comprised of 74% of Kennet (93) & 74% of North Wiltshire (93) & 61% of Salisbury (94) & 39% of Thamesdown (97) & 35% of West Wiltshire (94)

Worcestershire UA 1950-53: **100** 1959-63: **101** 1969-73: **86** 1981-85: **98** 1986-89: **97** 1990-92: **95** is comprised of 32% of Dudley (98) & 16% of Sandwell (105) & 52% of Bromsgrove (102) & 36% of Malvern Hills (97) & 83% of Redditch (90) & 38% of Wychavon (89) & 88% of Wyre Forest (97)

Worcestershire RD 1950-53: **91** 1959-63: **95** 1969-73: **95** 1981-85: **91** 1986-89: **95** 1990-92: **95** is comprised of 48% of Bromsgrove (102) & 15% of Leominster (99) & 35% of Malvern Hills (97) & 17% of Redditch (90) & 62% of Wychavon (89) & 12% of Wyre Forest (97)

Yorkshire, East Riding UA 1950-53: **94** 1959-63: **96** 1969-73: **98** 1981-85: **104** 1986-89: **103** 1990-92: **104** is comprised of 64% of Beverley (92) & 50% of East Yorkshire (102) & 40% of Holderness (100) & 7% of Ryedale (93) & 6% of Scarborough (100)

Yorkshire, East Riding RD 1950-53: **88** 1959-63: **92** 1969-73: **93** 1981-85: **91** 1986-89: **90** 1990-92: **93** is comprised of 36% of Beverley (92) & 27% of Boothferry (101) & 50% of East Yorkshire (102) & 60% of Holderness (100) & 8% of Ryedale (93) & 4% of Scarborough (100) & 24% of Selby (98)

Yorkshire, North Riding UA 1950-53: **106** 1959-63: **101** 1969-73: **106** 1981-85: **107** 1986-89: **106** 1990-92: **107** is comprised of 94% of Langbaurgh (107) & 14% of Stockton-on-Tees (108) & 12% of Hambleton (91) & 18% of Richmondshire (97) & 11% of Ryedale (93) & 63% of Scarborough (100)

Yorkshire, North Riding RD 1950-53: **93** 1959-63: **92** 1969-73: **107** 1981-85: **94** 1986-89: **91** 1990-92: **91** is comprised of 6% of Langbaurgh (107) & 23% of Middlesbrough (117) & 9% of Stockton-on-Tees (108) & 16% of Teesdale (99) & 88% of Hambleton (91) & 3% of Harrogate (104) & 82% of Richmondshire (97) & 74% of Ryedale (93) & 26% of Scarborough (100)

Yorkshire, West Riding UA 1950-53: **106** 1959-63: **106** 1969-73: **103** 1981-85: **105** 1986-89: **104** 1990-92: **103** is comprised of 11% of Oldham (116) & 61% of Barnsley (107) & 29% of Doncaster (101) & 24% of Rotherham (103) & 3% of Sheffield (104) & 42% of Bradford (110) & 49% of Calderdale (109) & 55% of Kirklees (106) & 30% of Leeds (101) & 59% of Wakefield (104) & 28% of Boothferry (101) & 18% of Pendle (99) & 27% of Craven (104) & 65% of Harrogate (104) & 14% of Selby (98)

Yorkshire, West Riding RD 1950-53: **96** 1959-63: **97** 1969-73: **96** 1981-85: **97** 1986-89: **97** 1990-92: **97** is comprised of 8% of Barnsley (107) & 45% of Doncaster (101) & 44% of Rotherham (103) & 12% of Sheffield (104) & 6% of Calderdale (109) & 7% of Leeds (101) & 22% of Wakefield (104) & 3% of South Lakeland (95) & 15% of Boothferry (101) & 11% of Ribble Valley (101) & 73% of Craven (104) & 32% of Harrogate (104) & 62% of Selby (98)

Welsh county remainders

Anglesey UA 1950-53: **110** 1959-63: **106** 1969-73: **100** 1981-85: **113** 1986-89: **104** 1990-92: **99** is comprised of 35% of Ynys Mon-Isle of Anglesey (94)

Anglesey RD 1950-53: **102** 1959-63: **107** 1969-73: **107** 1981-85: **89** 1986-89: **91** 1990-92: **91** is comprised of 65% of Ynys Mon-Isle of Anglesey (94)

Breconshire UA 1950-53: **111** 1959-63: **116** 1969-73: **111** 1981-85: **102** 1986-89: **107** 1990-92: **92** is comprised of 6% of Blaenau Gwent (108) & 26% of Brecknock (101)

Breconshire RD 1950-53: **99** 1959-63: **105** 1969-73: **109** 1981-85: **104** 1986-89: **101** 1990-92: **107** is comprised of 6% of Blaenau Gwent (108) & 3% of Cynon Valley (106) & 6% of Merthyr Tydfil (111) & 74% of Brecknock (101)

Caernarvonshire UA 1950-53: **102** 1959-63: **95** 1969-73: **95** 1981-85: **102** 1986-89: **97** 1990-92: **99** is comprised of 77% of Aberconwy (96) & 48% of Arfon (102) & 36% of Dwyfor (103)

Caernarvonshire RD 1950-53: **107** 1959-63: **105** 1969-73: **105** 1981-85: **100** 1986-89: **98** 1990-92: **102** is comprised of 8% of Aberconwy (96) & 52% of Arfon (102) & 64% of Dwyfor (103)

Cardiganshire UA 1950-53: **106** 1959-63: **109** 1969-73: **107** 1981-85: **121** 1986-89: **105** 1990-92: **95** is comprised of 27% of Ceredigion (97)

Cardiganshire RD 1950-53: **106** 1959-63: **99** 1969-73: **97** 1981-85: **90** 1986-89: **87** 1990-92: **98** is comprised of 73% of Ceredigion (97)

Camarthenshire UA 1950-53: **111** 1959-63: **112** 1969-73: **105** 1981-85: **116** 1986-89: **112** 1990-92: **100** is comprised of 26% of Carmarthen (99) & 36% of Dinefwr (105) & 48% of Llanelli (95)

Camarthenshire RD 1950-53: **109** 1959-63: **105** 1969-73: **113** 1981-85: **97** 1986-89: **94** 1990-92: **98** is comprised of 74% of Carmarthen (99) & 64% of Dinefwr (105) & 52% of Llanelli (95)

Denbighshire UA 1950-53: **99** 1959-63: **102** 1969-73: **99** 1981-85: **106** 1986-89: **106** 1990-92: **101** is comprised of 84% of Colwyn (100) & 42% of Glyndwr (97) & 34% of Wrexham Maelor (100) & 6% of Aberconwy (96)

Denbighshire RD 1950-53: **106** 1959-63: **97** 1969-73: **99** 1981-85: **95** 1986-89: **95** 1990-92: **98** is comprised of 16% of Colwyn (100) & 48% of Glyndwr (97) & 61% of Wrexham Maelor (100) & 9% of Aberconwy (96)

Flintshire UA 1950-53: **105** 1959-63: **103** 1969-73: **103** 1981-85: **105** 1986-89: **106** 1990-92: **100** is comprised of 38% of Alyn and Deeside (96) & 50% of Delyn (100) & 77% of Rhuddlan (97)

Flintshire RD 1950-53: **101** 1959-63: **96** 1969-73: **101** 1981-85: **96** 1986-89: **94** 1990-92: **97** is comprised of 62% of Alyn and Deeside (96) & 50% of Delyn (100) & 23% of Rhuddlan (97) & 5% of Wrexham Maelor (100)

Glamorganshire UA 1950-53: **115** 1959-63: **110** 1969-73: **110** 1981-85: **106** 1986-89: **106** 1990-92: **103** is comprised of 95% of Cynon Valley (106) & 5% of Merthyr Tydfil (111) & 53% of Ogwr (104) & 100% of Rhondda (110) & 67% of Rhymney Valley (105) & 37% of Taff-Ely (96) & 64% of Vale of Glamorgan (99) & 100% of Afan (98) & 51% of Lliw Valley (100) & 39% of Neath (107)

Glamorganshire RD 1950-53: **106** 1959-63: **106** 1969-73: **110** 1981-85: **100** 1986-89: **94** 1990-92: **97** is comprised of 2% of Cynon Valley (106) & 47% of Ogwr (104) & 7% of Rhymney Valley (105) & 63% of Taff-Ely (96) & 29% of Cardiff (99) & 36% of Vale of Glamorgan (99) & 49% of Lliw Valley (100) & 61% of Neath (107) & 10% of Swansea (98)

Merionethshire UA 1950-53: **111** 1959-63: **109** 1969-73: **108** 1981-85: **111** 1986-89: **111** 1990-92: **95** is comprised of 51% of Meirionnydd (92)

Merionethshire RD 1950-53: **105** 1959-63: **103** 1969-73: **101** 1981-85: **91** 1986-89: **95** 1990-92: **88** is comprised of 10% of Glyndwr (97) & 49% of Meirionnydd (92)

Monmouthshire UA 1950-53: **109** 1959-63: **109** 1969-73: **108** 1981-85: **107** 1986-89: **105** 1990-92: **104** is comprised of 88% of Blaenau Gwent (108) & 100% of Islwyn (97) & 38% of Monmouth (94) & 6% of Newport (103) & 89% of Torfaen (103) & 26% of Rhymney Valley (105)

Monmouthshire RD 1950-53: **98** 1959-63: **99** 1969-73: **103** 1981-85: **95** 1986-89: **92** 1990-92: **90** is comprised of 62% of Monmouth (94) & 18% of Newport (103) & 11% of Torfaen (103)

Montgomeryshire UA 1950-53: **102** 1959-63: **97** 1969-73: **104** 1981-85: **107** 1986-89: **104** 1990-92: **99** is comprised of 48% of Montgomery (91)

Montgomeryshire RD 1950-53: **95** 1959-63: **94** 1969-73: **84** 1981-85: **95** 1986-89: **89** 1990-92: **84** is comprised of 52% of Montgomery (91)

Pembrokeshire UA 1950-53: **110** 1959-63: **112** 1969-73: **112** 1981-85: **107** 1986-89: **101** 1990-92: **96** is comprised of 46% of Preseli (91) & 53% of South Pembrokeshire (94)

Pembrokeshire RD 1950-53: **99** 1959-63: **99** 1969-73: **104** 1981-85: **96** 1986-89: **95** 1990-92: **90** is comprised of 54% of Preseli (91) & 47% of South Pembrokeshire (94)

Radnorshire UA 1950-53: **101** 1959-63: **109** 1969-73: **94** 1981-85: **108** 1986-89: **102** 1990-92: **101** is comprised of 42% of Radnor (90)

Radnorshire RD 1950-53: **90** 1959-63: **83** 1969-73: **98** 1981-85: **87** 1986-89: **96** 1990-92: **83** is comprised of 58% of Radnor (90)

Scottish areas

Aberdeen Burgh (inc) 1950-53: **109** 1959-63: **107** 1969-73: **99** 1981-85: **112** 1986-89: **115** 1990-92: **110** is comprised of 75% of Aberdeen City (106)

Aberdeen County (rem) 1950-53: **99** 1959-63: **98** 1969-73: **95** 1981-85: **100** 1986-89: **97** 1990-92: **100** is comprised of 25% of Aberdeen City (106) & 80% of Banff and Buchan (101) & 100% of Gordon (101) & 19% of Kincardine and Deeside (105)

Arbroath Burgh 1950-53: **106** 1959-63: **110** 1969-73: **164** 1981-85: **111** 1986-89: **115** 1990-92: **115** is comprised of 24% of Angus (106)

Dundee County of City 1950-53: **116** 1959-63: **110** 1969-73: **106** 1981-85: **114** 1986-89: **117** 1990-92: **114** is comprised of 92% of Dundee City (115)

Angus County (rem) 1950-53: **104** 1959-63: **99** 1969-73: **101** 1981-85: **96** 1986-89: **106** 1990-92: **108** is comprised of 76% of Angus (106) & 8% of Dundee City (115)

Argyll County 1950-53: **109** 1959-63: **107** 1969-73: **108** 1981-85: **114** 1986-89: **117** 1990-92: **113** is comprised of 13% of Lochaber (111) & 88% of Argyll and Bute (112)

Ayr Burgh 1950-53: **107** 1959-63: **110** 1969-73: **108** 1981-85: **113** 1986-89: **108** 1990-92: **106** is comprised of 44% of Kyle and Carrick (107)

Kilmarnock Burgh 1950-53: **115** 1959-63: **119** 1969-73: **113** 1981-85: **114** 1986-89: **111** 1990-92: **108** is comprised of 59% of Kilmarnock and Loudoun (114)

Ayr County (rem) 1950-53: **107** 1959-63: **113** 1969-73: **112** 1981-85: **115** 1986-89: **114** 1990-92: **114** is comprised of 100% of Cumnock and Doon Valley (116) & 96% of Cunninghame (113) & 41% of Kilmarnock and Loudoun (114) & 56% of Kyle and Carrick (107)

Banff County 1950-53: **101** 1959-63: **108** 1969-73: **103** 1981-85: **108** 1986-89: **113** 1990-92: **109** is comprised of 20% of Banff and Buchan (101) & 31% of Moray (106)

Berwick County 1950-53: **110** 1959-63: **106** 1969-73: **98** 1981-85: **97** 1986-89: **97** 1990-92: **89** is comprised of 100% of Berwickshire (90) & 11% of Ettrick and Lauderdale (107)

Bute County 1950-53: **105** 1959-63: **105** 1969-73: **108** 1981-85: **111** 1986-89: **112** 1990-92: **110** is comprised of 12% of Argyll and Bute (112) & 4% of Cunninghame (113)

Caithness County 1950-53: **111** 1959-63: **112** 1969-73: **107** 1981-85: **120** 1986-89: **120** 1990-92: **115** is comprised of 100% of Caithness (115)

Clackmannan County 1950-53: **113** 1959-63: **108** 1969-73: **112** 1981-85: **111** 1986-89: **113** 1990-92: **108** is comprised of 100% of Clackmannan (108)

Clydebank Burgh 1950-53: **112** 1959-63: **115** 1969-73: **115** 1981-85: **116** 1986-89: **119** 1990-92: **120** is comprised of 77% of Clydebank (116)

Dumbarton Burgh 1950-53: **121** 1959-63: **122** 1969-73: **99** 1981-85: **126** 1986-89: **121** 1990-92: **127** is comprised of 27% of Dumbarton (114)

Dumbarton County (rem) 1950-53: **109** 1959-63: **108** 1969-73: **109** 1981-85: **101** 1986-89: **100** 1990-92: **100** is comprised of 100% of Bearsden and Milngavie (85) & 23% of Clydebank (116) & 80% of Cumbernauld and Kilsyth (104) & 73% of Dumbarton (114) & 3% of Renfrew (117) & 34% of Strathkelvin (107)

Dumfries Burgh 1950-53: **113** 1959-63: **111** 1969-73: **111** 1981-85: **116** 1986-89: **116** 1990-92: **115** is comprised of 48% of Nithsdale (114)

Dumfries County (rem) 1950-53: **101** 1959-63: **103** 1969-73: **104** 1981-85: **102** 1986-89: **102** 1990-92: **102** is comprised of 100% of Annandale and Eskdale (94) & 48% of Nithsdale (114)

East Lothian County 1950-53: **97** 1959-63: **104** 1969-73: **101** 1981-85: **98** 1986-89: **104** 1990-92: **101** is comprised of 74% of East Lothian (102)

Dunfermline Burgh 1950-53: **106** 1959-63: **109** 1969-73: **115** 1981-85: **105** 1986-89: **104** 1990-92: **112** is comprised of 37% of Dunfermline (107)

Kirkcaldy Burgh 1950-53: **113** 1959-63: **99** 1969-73: **102** 1981-85: **109** 1986-89: **114** 1990-92: **113** is comprised of 33% of Kirkcaldy (110)

Fife County (rem) 1950-53: **109** 1959-63: **107** 1969-73: **104** 1981-85: **109** 1986-89: **108** 1990-92: **107** is comprised of 63% of Dunfermline (107) & 67% of Kirkcaldy (110) & 100% of North East Fife (105)

Inverness Burgh 1950-53: **108** 1959-63: **104** 1969-73: **125** 1981-85: **107** 1986-89: **106** 1990-92: **101** is comprised of 48% of Inverness (103)

Inverness County (rem) 1950-53: **98** 1959-63: **100** 1969-73: **151** 1981-85: **109** 1986-89: **109** 1990-92: **106** is comprised of 70% of Badenoch and Strathspey (88) & 52% of Inverness (103) & 87% of Lochaber (111)

Insular Portion of Inverness County 1950-53: **105** 1959-63: **102** 1969-73: **111** 1981-85: **111** 1986-89: **118** 1990-92: **116** is comprised of 75% of Skye and Lochalsh (106) & 32% of Western Isles Islands (117)

Kincardine County (exc) 1950-53: **96** 1959-63: **98** 1969-73: **98** 1981-85: **101** 1986-89: **99** 1990-92: **105** is comprised of 81% of Kincardine and Deeside (105)

Kinross County 1950-53: **117** 1959-63: **101** 1969-73: **103** 1981-85: **104** 1986-89: **99** 1990-92: **95** is comprised of 8% of Perth and Kinross (107)

Kirkcudbright County 1950-53: **101** 1959-63: **107** 1969-73: **114** 1981-85: **104** 1986-89: **105** 1990-92: **103** is comprised of 4% of Nithsdale (114) & 100% of Stewartry (98) & 4% of Wigtown (113)

Airdrie Burgh 1950-53: **115** 1959-63: **116** 1969-73: **113** 1981-85: **113** 1986-89: **111** 1990-92: **127** is comprised of 41% of Monklands (127)

Coatbridge Burgh 1950-53: **120** 1959-63: **122** 1969-73: **111** 1981-85: **121** 1986-89: **121** 1990-92: **128** is comprised of 45% of Monklands (127)

Glasgow County of City 1950-53: **125** 1959-63: **125** 1969-73: **121** 1981-85: **126** 1986-89: **132** 1990-92: **131** is comprised of 88% of Glasgow City (128)

Hamilton Burgh 1950-53: **123** 1959-63: **119** 1969-73: **129** 1981-85: **123** 1986-89: **117** 1990-92: **119** is comprised of 37% of Hamilton (118)

Motherwell and Wishaw Burgh 1950-53: **115** 1959-63: **120** 1969-73: **118** 1981-85: **121** 1986-89: **119** 1990-92: **114** is comprised of 44% of Motherwell (121)

Rutherglen Burgh 1950-53: **118** 1959-63: **120** 1969-73: **115** 1981-85: **121** 1986-89: **122** 1990-92: **113** is comprised of 3% of Glasgow City (128)

Lanark County (rem) 1950-53: **114** 1959-63: **118** 1969-73: **114** 1981-85: **111** 1986-89: **111** 1990-92: **113** is comprised of 100% of East Kilbride (95) & 9% of Glasgow City (128) & 63% of Hamilton (118) & 100% of Lanark (now Clydesdale) (114) & 14% of Monklands (127) & 56% of Motherwell (121) & 52% of Strathkelvin (107)

Edinburgh Burgh 1950-53: **109** 1959-63: **109** 1969-73: **105** 1981-85: **108** 1986-89: **112** 1990-92: **114** is comprised of 93% of Edinburgh City (113)

Midlothian County (rem) 1950-53: **106** 1959-63: **107** 1969-73: **103** 1981-85: **105** 1986-89: **106** 1990-92: **104** is comprised of 1% of Ettrick and Lauderdale (107) & 26% of East Lothian (102) & 4% of Edinburgh City (113) & 100% of Midlothian (106) & 32% of West Lothian (110)

Moray County 1950-53: **100** 1959-63: **99** 1969-73: **100** 1981-85: **107** 1986-89: **104** 1990-92: **102** is comprised of 69% of Moray (106) & 30% of Badenoch and Strathspey (88)

Nairn County 1950-53: **102** 1959-63: **94** 1969-73: **115** 1981-85: **109** 1986-89: **113** 1990-92: **117** is comprised of 100% of Nairn (117)

Orkney County 1950-53: **103** 1959-63: **110** 1969-73: **102** 1981-85: **103** 1986-89: **114** 1990-92: **111** is comprised of 100% of Orkney Islands (111)

Peebles County 1950-53: **105** 1959-63: **100** 1969-73: **96** 1981-85: **107** 1986-89: **104** 1990-92: **104** is comprised of 100% of Tweeddale (104)

Perth Burgh 1950-53: **102** 1959-63: **105** 1969-73: **115** 1981-85: **108** 1986-89: **111** 1990-92: **112** is comprised of 29% of Perth and Kinross (107)

Perth County (rem) 1950-53: **98** 1959-63: **105** 1969-73: **98** 1981-85: **102** 1986-89: **104** 1990-92: **106** is comprised of 26% of Stirling (105) & 63% of Perth and Kinross (107)

Greenock Burgh 1950-53: **120** 1959-63: **125** 1969-73: **120** 1981-85: **123** 1986-89: **127** 1990-92: **130** is comprised of 57% of Inverclyde (124)

Paisley Burgh 1950-53: **117** 1959-63: **119** 1969-73: **110** 1981-85: **123** 1986-89: **121** 1990-92: **124** is comprised of 39% of Renfrew (117)

Port-Glasgow Burgh 1950-53: **126** 1959-63: **122** 1969-73: **120** 1981-85: **121** 1986-89: **128** 1990-92: **117** is comprised of 22% of Inverclyde (124)

Renfrew County (rem) 1950-53: **109** 1959-63: **108** 1969-73: **110** 1981-85: **106** 1986-89: **105** 1990-92: **106** is comprised of 100% of Eastwood (91) & 21% of Inverclyde (124) & 58% of Renfrew (117)

Ross and Cromarty County (rem) 1950-53: **100** 1959-63: **105** 1969-73: **180** 1981-85: **112** 1986-89: **106** 1990-92: **109** is comprised of 100% of Ross and Cromarty (107) & 25% of Skye and Lochalsh (106)

Insular Portion of Ross and Cromarty County 1950-53: **105** 1959-63: **95** 1969-73: **105** 1981-85: **112** 1986-89: **118** 1990-92: **112** is comprised of 68% of Western Isles Islands (117)

Roxburgh County 1950-53: **103** 1959-63: **109** 1969-73: **101** 1981-85: **108** 1986-89: **106** 1990-92: **116** is comprised of 20% of Ettrick and Lauderdale (107) & 100% of Roxburgh (113)

Selkirk County 1950-53: **105** 1959-63: **108** 1969-73: **104** 1981-85: **115** 1986-89: **104** 1990-92: **106** is comprised of 68% of Ettrick and Lauderdale (107)

Falkirk Burgh 1950-53: **108** 1959-63: **112** 1969-73: **106** 1981-85: **106** 1986-89: **116** 1990-92: **117** is comprised of 23% of Falkirk (114)

Stirling Burgh 1950-53: **107** 1959-63: **110** 1969-73: **100** 1981-85: **113** 1986-89: **115** 1990-92: **109** is comprised of 38% of Stirling (105)

Stirling County (rem) 1950-53: **108** 1959-63: **113** 1969-73: **110** 1981-85: **109** 1986-89: **113** 1990-92: **115** is comprised of 67% of Falkirk (114) & 36% of Stirling (105) & 20% of Cumbernauld and Kilsyth (104) & 14% of Strathkelvin (107)

Sutherland County 1950-53: **102** 1959-63: **102** 1969-73: **109** 1981-85: **113** 1986-89: **111** 1990-92: **110** is comprised of 100% of Sutherland (110)

West Lothian County 1950-53: **104** 1959-63: **103** 1969-73: **105** 1981-85: **109** 1986-89: **112** 1990-92: **110** is comprised of 11% of Falkirk (114) & 3% of Edinburgh City (113) & 68% of West Lothian (110)

Wigtown County 1950-53: **108** 1959-63: **120** 1969-73: **111** 1981-85: **114** 1986-89: **117** 1990-92: **112** is comprised of 96% of Wigtown (113)

Zetland County 1950-53: **110** 1959-63: **103** 1969-73: **103** 1981-85: **105** 1986-89: **107** 1990-92: **112** is comprised of 100% of Shetland Islands (112)

LIBRARY
PEMBURY HOSPITAL
01892 823535